THE NEW WAY TO
OF YOUR DREAMS

THE
PAT ENT
F RST
MAN FESTO

DR. BRYAN LASKIN

PRAISE FOR *THE PATIENT FIRST MANIFESTO*

"Bravo Dr. Bryan Laskin! *The Patient First Manifesto* has laid the foundation of 'must do's' for anyone leading a successful practice in today's modern world. He takes us on his own journey, both personally and professionally, to realize our own measuring stick in life. It takes a shift in mindset to grow a successful business, stay relevant and to always put patients first. Lucky for us, Bryan has transformed his passion, leadership skills and expertise by giving back to an industry that did so much for him."

Pam Borton
CEO & Founder: ON Point Next Level Leadership
TeamWomen: Founder & Board Chair
Empower Leadership Academy: Founder
ICF MCC Senior Executive Coach

"This book isn't just a glimpse into the future of healthcare, it's the roadmap to get there. On behalf of patients everywhere, thank you, Dr. Bryan Laskin, for showing other providers how innovation, technology and a patient-first mindset can positively and fundamentally change health care."

Kristi Piehl
CEO & Founder: Media Minefield

"Dr. Laskin and his team have developed some amazing tools to make dentistry a smooth experience not only for dental professionals, but even more so for patients. From improving the clinical experience with OperaDDS to the patient experience with OperaVR, and not to mention the skills and connections taught with Upgrade Dental, Dr. Laskin and his team have not only improved the world of dentistry, they have transformed it."

Dr. Brandon Tiek
Tiek Dental Studio

"Vital and indispensable. The Patient First Manifesto is a must-read for dentists who want to take it to the next level"

Pedram Nastaean
CEO: Kwikly Dental Staffing

"In a few short pages, Dr. Laskin has perfectly summed up the disconnect that exists between the practice of dentistry and the business of dentistry. With short stories and simple tips along the way, he bridges that gap and not only shows you how to massively improve your business, but also how to future proof your practice by leveraging technology and efficiency. As long time users of the OperaDDS suite of dental technology, it's awesome to see Dr. Laskin continue to give back to the dental community by teaching others to improve the profession through a better patient experience."

Michael Cruz
Dee For Dentist

"I LOVE *The Patient First Manifesto!* It is to the point, extremely helpful and should become every dental office's bible."

Deborah Carrier, RDH
Founder: Twice As Nice Uniforms

"We are recent converts to OperaDDS, and are enjoying how it combines many functions that we previously had several different vendors for. And doing them better, and for less cost. This book will be read by all of our Team here at White Bear Smiles, and inspire us to do even more to help our patients. The Patient First Manifesto is a great book for dentistry moving forward."

Paul Anderson, DDS
White Bear Smiles

"Everyone from your auxiliary staff to upper-level management should read and reread this book over time. It touches base on why you must put patients first. And when that happens, everyone wins."

Yomiyu Hirpa
President: Kwikly Dental Staffing

"*The Patient First Manifesto* is fantastic! A very personal experience of successful tools to bring your practice to greatness! Very interesting read and kept me captivated to read more. *The Patient First Manifesto* and its content should be required reading in dental schools. This book contains the key gems to guide anin the efficient delivery of good patient care."

Janel Fish
CRDA, CEREC Instructor

"*The Patient First Manifesto* is an exceptional work of art. This book is incredible, entertaining and insightful! I was literally laughing out loud many times while reading. Wow!! *The Patient*

First Manifesto is amazing, informative and amusing!! Dr. Bryan Laskin is a great writer and hilarious. I could visualize every scenario that was provided."

Kelcey Trefethen
Program Manager: Amazon
Adaptive Leader

"Dr. Bryan Laskin's *The Patient Manifesto,* has come just in time to save dentistry from itself! Written with humility *and* guts, Dr. Laskin lays out how we got here as an industry and what we can do to pivot our POV. Dr. Laskin lays out changemaking & thought innovation in his must-read, breakout book helping us cross the chasm into the post COVID-19 marketplace that eagerly awaits our passion, compassion and contribution to overall patient wellness. High marks to Dr. Laskin for his deep understanding of patient preferences, psycho-demographics and health consumerism. Both humorous and thought provoking, *The Patient Manifesto* elevates the game for us all."

Angelique Swann
Director: Implant Empowerment

Like many skilled technicians that have invested time and money to master their craft, dentists often pay too little attention to the wide range of experiential factors driving the satisfaction of their customers. Dr. Laskin shines a laser light on these deeply neglected aspects of the dental business, offering thoughtful and compelling analysis, complete with the diagnosis and prescription for his peers.

Steven Ostrover
President: Futuredontics

THE PATIENT FIRST MANIFESTO
THE NEW WAY TO BUILD THE PRACTICE
OF YOUR DREAMS

DR. BRYAN LASKIN

109 Bushaway Road, Suite 100
Wayzata, MN 55391
upgradedental.com

ISBN print book 978-1-7366437-1-6

ISBN ebook 978-1-7366437-2-3

This book is dedicated to:

My wife, Tesa, my daughter, Naiya, and my son, Miles:
You are all amazing, supportive people who I am lucky
and proud to love with all my heart.

And also:
Megan Hennen
Martin Helmbrecht
Nate Johnson
David Pryor
Aleh Matus

You are living proof that a small group of dedicated people
is the most powerful force in the world.

The Patient First Manifesto

WE STRIVE TO IMPROVE CARE BECAUSE WE VALUE:

team over **self**

   patients over **procedures**

     and

      adaptation over **stagnation**.

WE KNOW THAT WHEN PATIENTS WIN, WE ALL WIN.

Table of

Contents

THE
PATIENT
FIRST
MANIFESTO

Introduction

MY GLOVED HANDS CAREFULLY LAID THE MIRROR AND explorer out on the white paper tray cover as I carefully ran through the steps in my head of the upcoming extraction. I had just purchased the practice less than a week ago, and I was exceptionally excited to perform the first extraction in my new office.

Normally I would have been worried about the clinical outcome, as extractions are not my specialty, but the radiograph that I had just finished reviewing showed that this baby tooth was barely hanging to the tissue. One hard sneeze and this kid, who was already waiting in the reception area, would likely do the work for me.

I impatiently loomed over the poor assistant while she loaded the anesthetic syringe, and I made sure she placed every forceps we had in the practice out on the tray...just in case we needed them.

I love working on kids and particularly love extracting single sided retained canines, like this one. Anesthetic is easy to place painlessly. The round root, completely resorbed, makes the extraction usually possible with a simple quick rotation of your wrist.

I was ready. The operatory was perfectly set up. I hadn't met the boy that this tooth was attached to yet, as he had just been referred over by an orthodontist, but we were both surely going to celebrate my magnificent technique and his easy, pain-free extraction in just a few minutes.

With the table set, so to speak, I couldn't wait to get started. I even knew the toy I was going to give my young patient at the end of the appointment (one of those little water filled basketball hoop games).

After hiding in the small office for a few minutes and letting the friendly dental assistant seat my lucky patient, I decided it was time to enter the operatory and dazzle this kid with my wit and exceptional dental skills.

As I entered the room, this cute little 8 year old boy quickly whipped his head around and looked up at me through vengeful, hostile eyes and instantly shouted, "I hate you!"

He proceeded to leap out of the dental chair and cling to his father's leg as if it were attached to a helicopter that he was dangling from 25,000 feet above the ground.

We didn't finish his extraction that day. Instead this young man incessantly cried and wailed to his father that I was a cruel man, intent on hurting him and that he would not stand for it.

My heart sank. I felt like a complete failure that day.

While I attempted to refer him to the pedodontist, the boy ended up coming back the next day without an appointment. Much to my surprise, we were actually able to easily complete the extraction.

In fact, the little boy apologized immediately as I entered the room. Then, after telling me how sorry he was about the prior day's incident, he promptly stated, "I won't cause you any problems today," and opened his mouth as wide as he could, as if to try to mimic a snake getting ready to eat an alligator.

All the while he never diverted his eyes from his mother who, in the corner of the room, looked back at him through a gaze that could freeze hellfire.

I learned an important lesson that day; sometimes the biggest factor in the success of our clinical outcomes is which parent brings the kid to the office.

This was not what I thought being a dentist would be like.

Like many of you, I became a doctor to help people. I wanted to work with my hands, in my own business that directly and positively affected people everyday. So, becoming a dentist seemed like a natural fit.

I, however, had never had a filling done, or even had orthodontics prior to going to dental school. I had no idea what I was getting myself into.

The reality of being a dentist has been drastically different than what I imagined. I consider myself an upbeat, positive person, but through the vast majority of my career, I have felt dissatisfied and dejected by my patients.

I believe any dentist would tell you that this is a natural part of being a dentist.

While I have worked hard to help everyone in my care, the way patients respond to dental care has often made me feel like I was punishing them. Not so subtly, patients have proudly proclaimed they "hate the dentist", demanded that I don't "hurt them" or cried the moment I entered the room.

Like many caregivers, it has been easy for me to focus on the complainers and overlook the positive comments from patients that seem to be few and far between.

I often would dream that I became a jeweler, like my grandfather; or, as I like to joke, of selling snow cones by the ocean. Nobody is scared, anxious or depressed when buying jewelry or snow cones.

Being a doctor or care team member is hard. There are certainly less stressful ways to make as much or more money. Most of us, however, truly went into this profession to help our patients elevate their health and live a better life. Helping others be healthier is probably the most noble of callings, but being a caregiver can oftentimes be a brutal profession.

For me to reconcile the paradox between trying to help people everyday and the fact that they hated coming to my office, I have obsessed over creating the ideal patient experience. I have had the honor of developing technologies that enhance dentistry both with my team and in concert with some of the most progressive dental companies.

Through this work I have unexpectedly uncovered the simple reasons why some offices are thriving more than ever today, as others are dying quickly. The secret keys as to why well-meaning doctors, including physicians, fail greatly in meeting the expectations of their patients and their teams.

The Patient First Manifesto expands what the definition of quality care is and describes how to achieve the practice of your dreams.

Putting patients first does not mean your clinical care needs to be flawless. Regardless of how great your clinical work is, for your office to thrive today you must focus on some fundamental conveniences that patients expect. This includes recognizing that **phone calls are archaic, film X-rays are outdated and paper is filthy.** If you do not believe this to be true, I assure you your patients do. And they are right.

If you believe that the current state of patient care is just fine and are unwilling to make even the simplest of alterations to grow your practice, this book is not for you.

If, however, you are a doctor or team member who wishes to elevate your care, The Patient First Manifesto will make you more money with less stress.

If you are a patient, this book will show you why a generation of well meaning dentists have unknowingly propagated the reasons why people hate going to the dentist.

The Patient First Manifesto will detail the experiences that team members and patients are expecting today. There have been fundamental shifts in the economic marketplace, shifts that include the dental and medical industries. Yet these industries have largely ignored these changes.

Ultimately this has hurt doctors, team members and patients tremendously.

Addressing these expectations will increase your case acceptance, elevate the population's health and grow your profitability.

The knowledge contained in this book comes from 20 years of constantly asking myself one simple question:

How do patients want their care delivered?

It seems simple enough, but this question is unintentionally overlooked by the vast majority of doctors and team members every day. They are rightfully focused almost exclusively on delivering high clinical quality care in an ever increasingly difficult business and consumer environment.

In the chapters that follow, you will find out what The Great Disconnect between doctors and their patients is, how it came to be and how overcoming this barrier will grow your practice beyond what you thought was possible.

This book includes several personal stories. For purposes of privacy and respecting those involved, all names other than my family members have been changed.

If you would like download free tools to upgrade your care go to ThePatientFirstManifesto.com/Free

1.

Patient Vs. Doctor

*"It has long been an axiom of mine that the little
things are infinitely the most important."*

- Arthur Conan Doyle

IT WAS AN EXTRAORDINARY CASE. TEN ANTERIOR
maxillary veneers on a beautiful 25 year old patient with a
history of bulimia. Julie was well out of treatment for her
eating disorder and healthy for the last few years, but she had
the unfortunate stain that was left from her disease; a mouth
full of caries and excessively worn and fractured teeth.

Her upper incisors and premolars had the classic erosion
leftover from her disease, and even if you were not a dentist,
you would recognize there was "something wrong" with her
mouth. Julie still felt the sting of previous bullying and having
her young niece consistently ask, "Why are your teeth brown?"

Fully aware of what was at stake, I carefully planned out Julie's restorations. Countless hours were devoted to model work, wax ups and consultations with Julie explaining the procedure, the steps involved and how we could restore her mouth. I even had two phone conversations with Julie's mother, a retired hygienist, to convince her family that I was the man for the job.

The preparations went smoothly. The temporaries carefully sculpted the tissue after a little laser recontouring.

The end result was even better than I could have imagined.

Julie's mother had sent photos of what Julie looked like before the damage and made me promise to restore her daughter's smile. I said I could only do my best.

But in the end, the result actually achieved this lofty goal.

Julie cried tears of joy when she looked in the mirror. Her self confidence and dentition were restored. This is exactly what we, in dentistry, live for.

So, seeing that Julie had left a 5 star Google review only increased my pride in the accomplishment.

When I read that 5 star review, however, my pride vanished and a wave of disappointment crashed over me.

Julie's review did not hold a single mention of the phone calls to her crying mother, the therapy sessions in the dental chair, the meticulous communication with the laboratory technician, the artistic veneers or even the fact that her smile was restored at all (let alone the beautiful results we achieved).

Julie's review, instead, mentioned that our office was fantastic because we always ran on time and that we offered "the best coffee" in our reception.

This review caused an existential crisis to erupt in my brain. On the one hand, I was happy that I had another satisfied patient, but on the other hand... WTF? Right?!?!

The Keurig coffee pot I picked up on a whim from Target got highlighted in the review and my extraordinary attention to detail in this case, as well as my clinical prowess, was completely ignored. Our refreshments had more significance to Julie than the quality of care we delivered.

But Julie's case is not the exception, this is genuinely how most people judge our practices today.

In fact, research has shown that in 2020 twenty-eight percent of medical patients switched providers due to a poor digital health experience.[1] That means that since the COVID-19 pandemic, more than 1 in 4 patients actually left their doctors solely due to their digital experience, or the lack thereof.

Ask dentists what is important in dental care and you will likely hear terms like fit, accuracy, symmetry and shade match. If you ask patients what is important to them in dentistry, they will mention words like convenience, nice, white, clean and painless.

This different perspective frustrates dentists to no end. I see comments on social media every day that highlight similar patient perspectives. My favorite thread on the popular community platform DentalTown, titled "GTFOOMO", or Get The F Out of My Office, details similar interactions from the dentists' perspective. At the writing of this book,

---

[1] "2020 Healthcare Consumer Experience Study", Cedar, 2020.

the thread is 664 pages long and over 33,000 posts. The first post on this thread sarcastically states wanting to punch someone in the face when mentioning they hate needles. Needles, however, are the number one reason that people hate going to the dentist.

That's a lot of people to punch in the face everyday.

But in these maddeningly frustrating interactions with patients there are the diamonds that can be mined to build that practice you always dreamed of.

If we truly listen to patients and uncover what they are looking for in their version of quality care, we can find the keys that unlock the door to that multi-million dollar practice that runs itself so that you can just focus on dentistry. Where profitability is over thirty percent, your team comes to work excited to be there and patients are grateful for the care your team provides.

This is the reality that we deal with every day— both patients and professionals. Addressing this toxic environment is long overdue. A simple mindset shift is all that is required to find a better way.

The truth is that focusing on what patients care about is what will allow your practice to thrive, and ignoring your patients' perspective can kill your practice.

There are many easy "coffee pots" that you can add to your practice that will allow you to see more patients, have higher profits and lower your stress. Incorporating these simple benefits may, at first, seem like they are only conveniences that you need to implement to placate picky patients. But, ultimately, it is these easy patient accommodations that will quickly build your reputation and lead to a career that is more prosperous than you would ever be able to build through clinical mastery.

Patients care about efficient appointments, comfort, extended hours and a clean office. This translates into your office needing paperless forms, easy payments, new sedation options, and an uncluttered office environment.

By providing these easy conveniences for patients, you will be able to finally afford that CAD/CAM system or Cone Beam that you may be drooling over, but costs over a hundred thousand dollars. This is the counter-intuitive truth; the easy to overlook, inexpensive conveniences we provide for our patients will eventually generate the additional revenue required to pay for whatever facility, technology or tools you desire to build the practice of your dreams.

The irony lies in the fact dentists convince themselves that they are buying the Cone Beam for their patients, but typically fail to ever even communicate the value of this wonderful technology to those in their care.

In the pages of this book, I will show you how to easily uncover these diamonds and use them to catapult your practice forward. Whether you currently own a practice, provide clinical care, manage a practice, are a member of the office care team or are a curious patient, I applaud you for taking the time and energy to learn more about what is broken in today's patient experiences and applying yourself to improve the care in your practice.

2.

Patient Vs. Profit

"It is literally true that you can succeed best and quickest by helping others to succeed."

- Napoleon Hill

AT LEAST UP TO THE TIME OF WRITING THIS BOOK, I have never had a cavity. I did not have orthodontics as a kid. Also, a rarity in dentistry, I am the only member of my family who has had a career in dentistry.

I never even had an acquaintance who worked in dentistry prior to dental school.

Consequently, in dental school, my lack of dental knowledge was a great source of insecurity. At one point, I timidly approached a dental instructor that I trusted and asked, "Will patients trust me if I've never even had a cavity?"

To this day I remember my tremendous relief when he replied, "How many cardiologists do you think have had a heart attack?"

Personally, I have never had a negative dental experience, but early in my career I realized a simple truth; patients do not like being in the dental operatory chair. In fact, most people would rather do just about anything else.

Here are some things people would rather do than undergo a dental procedure that prove this point.[2]

- 33% would go without sex for a month
- 30% would spend a whole day at work
- 19% would speak in front of a crowd of 50+ people (the greatest fear for 40% of Americans[3])

When I purchased my first practice, I became acutely aware of another crucial fact that also aided in my future success; the less time it takes to do a procedure the more profitable I was doing that procedure. So, taking less time to do procedures equals more money.

This should be obvious to us all, but many dental professionals would be shocked if they knew how much time is wasted everyday in their practice. If you would like to see how you are doing, just ask your team how much time you

---

[2] survey conducted by OnePoll with a sample of 2,000 US adults, September 2017

[3] Gallup poll 2014

spend chit-chatting with people. You'll likely be shocked at the answer.

Thankfully, my eyes were opened to this early in my career. I also quickly recognized the fact that the easiest way to improve my clinical quality, while also reducing the time it took to do each procedure, was to look for small, incremental improvements each time I did that procedure.

There is great long-lasting power in seeking out the small adjustments to tweak and improve your work, versus looking for large radical changes. These tweaks compound over time to quickly become faster and of much higher quality than you can imagine.

So, right away I documented how I did every single procedure in my office, and depended on everyone in the practice to look for small improvements that I could add over time.

When I first started producing CAD/CAM restorations in my office is a good example of this working in my practice. My first CAD/CAM onlay was done on tooth #3 in the mouth of one of my best friends.

It is a good thing that I did this on him first, as that onlay took over four and a half hours.

However, we captured every single aspect of that appointment and looked for ways to improve the next restoration and each one after that. We swapped out silanes, ordered more efficient burs, changed how we imaged and even timed each different ceramic block's milling time (making sure to use the same restoration, so we knew we were removing all other variables).

This led to every procedure delivering more consistent results in less time. Within one year, that same onlay would be scheduled for an hour and usually be done early.

In other words, by documenting each procedure and performing that procedure the same way each time, except for potentially one seemingly insignificant improvement, you will end up achieving better results in less time.

This was proven in a study published in the Harvard Business Review, which showed that shorter times spent in the hospital after surgery leads to better outcomes[4]. Shorter stays, therefore, are better for patients, doctors, team members and the practices as a whole.

Many doctors, however, feel like each tooth should be treated like a unique challenge. A snowflake to be rediscovered each time that same procedure is performed. I, however, believe that it is much more productive to look for whatever consistencies we can in each similar procedure, and incrementally improve them to achieve the best results.

The desire to treat each procedure uniquely is, I believe, why many dentists feel that reducing the time it takes to do procedures is equal to "cutting corners" or trading to do lower quality care in the greedy pursuit of profits.

But, as I just described:

1. Patients want procedures to take as little time as possible to get the best results
2. More efficient procedures are more profitable

---

[4] David W. Larson. *Harvard Business Review* (Online) 10/15/19

3. More consistent procedures lead to faster and higher quality care

These three truths detail how efficiency can be done right within healthcare. So, if we strive for excellence in our care, we must also focus on increasing our efficiency. Ultimately, many doctors are not aware of the crucial reality that striving for efficiency is not just more profitable, but also vital to improving care and benefiting patients' care experiences.

These three truths also highlight one primary reason that I chose healthcare as my career; when healthcare is done well, everybody wins.

This seems to some to be impossible, or at best counter-intuitive, but it is quite true and it is actually quite easy to achieve wins for everyone in dentistry, all the time.

This is not always, or even usually, the case in business. Restaurants make more if they sell more alcohol and desserts, resulting in their customers becoming less healthy and fatter. Car dealerships make more if they sell you warranties that they know is almost all profit for the dealership and a losing bet for the customer. Health and dental insurance companies… Well, we all can detail many negative experiences that have lined the pockets of these companies and built their towers in every major city.

In contrast to this, we helping patients helps us in return. To illustrate this point, let's examine how I segment the dental patient population and what happens when we move patients to an elevated category.

The levels of dental patient care fall into 3 categories:

1. Emergency
2. Maintenance
3. Optimal

Emergency patients only come in if they have a true or perceived dental emergency. These patients typically have swelling, pain or some other condition that drives them to come to the office. Our primary goal, as caregivers for these patients, is to help them see the benefits inherent in elevating their oral health from emergency to maintenance care. Doing this will avoid future emergencies which can be costly, inconvenient and potentially life threatening.

If patients move up from emergency to maintenance care, they will feel better, look better and they will avoid unnecessary costs that they may not have planned for and they may not be able to afford when they need it.

While emergency patients can be profitable for the practice, it is typically maintenance patients who make up the true life blood of our profitability, as we can rely on their recurring revenue on a regular basis and they come in more frequently to have more care. Also, we can leverage treatment that is performed by more auxiliary team members in maintenance care, which is obviously more profitable.

Maintenance patients, unlike emergency patients, come in regularly to the office for care. If it is urgent, they will likely complete their needed treatment. With maintenance patients, however, there is also some remaining treatment that they would benefit from that they are not completing. This may be because the additional treatment is viewed as optional, but it can often be delayed or treatment that is flat out refused by the maintenance patient because they did not see the value in the more optimal care. In many cases maintenance patients do not complete their optimal treatment options because they were not educated effectively by the doctor or team member in the practice.

But if the patient does move from maintenance care to optimal care they will look better and feel better. Also, moving people from maintenance care to optimal care oftentimes leads to the most profitable procedures a practice can perform. Examples of optimal care procedures that are quite profitable include implants, orthodontics and cosmetic services like veneers.

In summary, moving patients from emergency to maintenance care or maintenance to optimal treatment is a win for everyone. By tracking if you are doing more treatment on more patients, you will have a fairly good indication that you are doing this well.

This is why going over production numbers, as well as the number of each individual procedure you do with the whole team is valuable. These numbers mirror the quality of care you are providing your patients.

Oftentimes team members perceive discussing practice numbers to be greedy, or motivated by profit. In reality, the only way we can quantify the work we do in elevating our patients' health is in analysing the metrics that reflect that care we deliver.

So, how do we use these truths in our daily practice to both improve our care and our profitability? The first step is to actively look for ways that you can improve your care and be more efficient. These improvements can come in a multitude of sources, but be sure to ask yourself this single question every time you are looking to implement any piece of technology, procedure or change in your practice:

Does this benefit our patient, our team and our practice?

If the answer is "yes" to all three, do not hesitate to incorporate whatever you are looking to implement. A great example of something that instantly benefits everyone is paperless forms. From less cross contamination, to relieving overworked business office team members and more accurate information in the clinic— there is absolutely no downside to anyone. Paperless forms even cost less than paper forms (by an order of magnitude).

If the answer is "yes" to only one or two, you must decide if the innovation negatively affects the others. For example, CAD/CAM restorations benefit patients with less time in the office and better outcomes, but your team and practice will need to be trained on how to have the system work in your practice. In short, if you aren't willing to do the front end work, it may not be the best time to incorporate CAD/CAM in your practice, as it will end up not working out for anyone.

Obviously, if the initiative doesn't benefit patients, your team or your practice, it should not be adopted, or removed as quickly as possible. I would argue film X-rays, paper charts, amalgam restorations and the way dental reimbursement "insurance" works today are all aspects of dental care that are archaic and should be sunsetted by our profession as quickly as possible.

To learn more about how to easily select and implement technology in your practice go to ThePatientFirstManifesto.com/Free

3.

The Great Disconnect

"Never let formal education get in the way
of your learning."

—Mark Twain

I HAD JUST FINISHED A LECTURE AT A MAJOR DENTAL conference and went to grab lunch before catching my flight out of Vegas. I saw a big group of friendly looking people, so I sat down and started chatting with them.

The entire table of eight people worked in the same dental office from Austin, Texas. The practice had two dentists and I was sitting next to the sole owner. As I know this affable group was not in my lecture, I asked the dentist next to me if he saw any good lectures at the meeting.

His response blew me away.

He quickly replied, "I always go to Dr. Kline's course on dental bonding and I always love it! This was the seventh time I've seen it and it was the best. It's great because it is the same exact course everytime and I learn something new each time."

Up to that point, whenever I lectured, I made sure to never give the same lecture twice, as I was worried I would bore someone in the audience who heard the information before. Man, was I wrong.

The Austin dentist's love of watching the same dentin bonding lecture seven years in a row made me realize that, as Samuel Johnson said, "People need to be reminded more often than they need to be instructed."

Since then I've also come to learn that dentists tend to wander trade show floors and attend courses at conventions almost exclusively looking for ways to improve their clinical dentistry, just as we tend to primarily focus on the clinical care in our practices.

However, much of the information to be found within the confines of your average dental convention is something that we all have likely learned before. For example, the courses at these conventions on dental bonding will be overflowing, yet dental bonding hasn't fundamentally changed in over a quarter century.

Doctors, like most people, prefer to have their under-standing validated instead of expanded. We would rather relearn something we know to be true, rather than have to go through the discomfort of having our beliefs challenged or learn something new. This can be a large barrier in evolv-ing yourself or your practice.

Another even less effective use of one's time and energy than refreshing your memory when continuing your professional education, is attempting to learn something new that we can not put into practice or ever hope to understand completely.

For example, allow me to save you the enormous amount of hours that the aforementioned dentists spent attempting to learn more about dental bonding every year with just a few words:

Read the freaking manual!

Having spent time with some amazing chemists at several dental manufacturers, I can tell you they know more about the bonding agents they produce than any dentist could hope to learn in the course of their career. Yet, no matter how many courses you go to, they will all likely be presented by another dentist who talked to that chemist for an hour or so.

These chemists' whole careers are focused entirely on studying and improving dental bonding, so they don't have time to go out and lecture to dentists about what they do in the laboratory.

The best they can do to help us is distill their knowledge down to a few pictograms showing how to best use their product, as they know that even following those few wordless descriptors may be too lofty an expectation of us.

Today, every reputable bonding agent works well. Just meticulously use the system as it was designed to be used and you will obtain great results. If you have problems with debonds, I can assure you that the problem is not the bonding agent's fault. The failure surely falls in the technique used to apply to the bonding agent itself. So, review the pictograms again, check your preparation and control the isolation while you follow the instructions.

Meanwhile, the half filled room next to the bonding course could be featuring industry changing innovations like teledentistry, Therapeutic Virtual Reality (TVR), and Artificial Intelligence (AI). Innovations that completely transform the patient experience and have massive potential to rocket your practice to new heights.

But, just as it is not necessary to learn all there is to know about bonding in order to benefit from the tremendous work these chemists do to improve our dentistry, there is no need for you to know everything about these new technologies for them to enhance your practice.

The value to your practice and to your patients lies solely in applying new technology to address a current problem or unlock a new opportunity, not in learning everything about the technology itself.

Think about it this way, we all use mobile phones to be more productive, yet most of us have just a passing idea about how the internet leverages 5G signals or ethernet to send a traditional email through multiple servers to go from your office to the specialist.

All we, as guardians of our patients' electronic health information, really need to understand is that those servers that the traditional email goes through are not secure enough and put our patients' information at risk, so we must use a secure email platform to transfer and protect this crucial data.

As Steve Jobs stated, "...ideas are worth nothing unless executed. They are just a multiplier. Execution is worth millions."

In fact, the desire to exclusively educate yourself about information you either already know or we can not actually apply can distract you from learning about what patients really would like to have implemented in your practice. When going to tradeshows and continuing education, it can be most valuable to look for ways to expand your practice to include new aspects of care from your patients' perspective, not your own.

Sometimes this can be a new clinical procedure, such as implants or a new technique that is more efficient and predictable. Many times, however, we seek out information that really does nothing to elevate our care, as in the example of going to the same course describing the chemistry of dental bonding seven years in a row.

The noble pursuit of providing the highest quality dentistry can end up distancing ourselves from how patients view our care and diminishes our knowledge of their perspective overall. In other words, by trying to help patients, we can end up distancing ourselves from them.

This reality was revealed to me when I recently asked a dentist who I admire (and who happens to chair a prestigious committee on Standard development at the ADA),

"Why is there such a lack of patients represented in the dental Standardization practice?" His reply was, "How would patients know what they need?"

This is the view of the current leadership in our industry. And it is wrong.

I understand that when selecting composites, figuring out when to treatment plan scaling and root planing, or even determining the best financial options to offer in our office, we have to know what is in the best interest for everyone and patients should have little to no say. Patients can not be expected to make uniformed clinical decisions without our guidance, and they can not be expected to know all the variables that go into running a thriving dental practice.

But, when it comes to many details of how we deliver our care, blatantly ignoring the patients' experience ends up hurting everyone. Both literally and figuratively hurting everyone, through the propagation of anxiety that leads to lower case acceptance, lower quality of care, more painful procedures and stress induced negative consequences for all.

This is what I call "The Great Disconnect"; our dogmatic pursuit of quality dentistry combined with our empathy, leading to two distinct perspectives in how our care is delivered— the perspective of the caregiver and the perspective of the dental patient.

What is most troubling is that both perspectives are true, but only patients seem to be aware of both sides of the equation. They obviously want and need us to perform high quality care but, in this day and age, the quality of our care is assumed.

This assumption of the highest quality of care is the origin of the 5 star Google reviews that discuss our coffee and not our care. In my patient's mind, we could only produce amazing results or we were a total failure. Quality care, therefore, is expected by patients today.

We can complain about this, but the reality is that patients do not know, and can not be expected to understand, the differences between poor care, adequate care and what is truly exceptional care. Therefore, they look for other ways to judge us and our teams.

So, they end up judging us by seemingly moronic aspects of our practice like the quality of coffee we provide.

Patients also expect us to care as much as they do about how they view their care beyond their oral health needs. This isn't hard to figure out, yet we, as an industry, are largely ignoring these basic desires.

Patients care about simple things that we often neglect: paperless intake forms, clutter-free operatories, the ability to update medical histories from your phone, touchless payment processing, pain-free injections, multiple sedation options, easy recall notices, the ability to give negative feedback to your team and not being lectured.

The bad news is that, currently, offices largely ignore these patients' needs and still seem to not look beyond the clinical delivery of care.

The good news is that applying these tools that will elevate the patient experience and allow your practice to thrive are relatively inexpensive, easy to implement and readily available.

The key is to get started. Once you shift your mindset and start adopting technology to unlock some small opportunities in your practice effectively, new opportunities will present themselves.

Securing small wins from implementing easy changes in your practice will lead you to going for bigger wins over time.

Take, for example, the first technology that I implemented in my practice: a digital calendar.

No, I do not mean online scheduling or digital chart notes… I am talking about our daily schedule that contains all our appointments. You see, when I bought my first practice in 2001, we had a big physical book in which we penciled in people's appointments. It looked straight out of Hogwarts and smelled like it too.

Knowing that I knew nothing about running a practice, I hired a local dental practice consultant and she immediately told me that, in order to grow the practice, it was vitally important that we ditch the big book and put our schedules on the big CRT monitor that glowed at the front desk.

I was horrified and petrified. How would I know what my schedule looked like?! I had my personal calendar on my Palm device, but this was a totally different animal, right?

Well, needless to say, my concerns were not only unfounded, but losing the physical scheduling book and having a digital calendar was a huge time saver for everyone and led to more consistent, higher quality care.

I am sure that when patients came to my practice in 2001, they were mortified that we still had a physical calendar that was being used to schedule their care. I was just oblivious to this fact.

While the days of the paper schedule have long passed in most dental offices today, there remain many outdated techniques, protocols and procedures that we use in our practices.

It is time to move on. There is simply too much at stake.

4.

What's At Stake

"A brand for a company is like a reputation for a person. You earn reputation by trying to do hard things well."

- Jeff Bezos

My wife, Tesa, has tons of friends. She connects strongly with people and texts dozens of people by 7 AM every day. Sometimes I swear smoke emanates from the phone as her thumbs fly over the screen like a hovering hummingbird's wings.

Tesa is also a very caring person. If my cousin's mother-in-law's friend breaks her foot, you can be assured that Tesa will share tears with family members and be shocked at my lack of visible concern.

Tesa also deeply values health and wellness. From scheduling family yoga every week, to making sure everything we all eat is organic whole foods, she makes sure our family is as healthy as possible. When she finds a new, more nutritious alternative to sprouted bread, not only does she make sure it is on hand at our house, she makes sure to grab some for all her friends to be certain that they are all informed.

In other words, Tesa is the ideal patient. She is focused on optimal health and is a champion who refers others. She also cares deeply about relationships, and would never leave a caregiver she trusts.

This is why I was completely shocked when Tesa made me an appointment for a new eye doctor.

Not only was our (now) old eye doctor a talented clinician and an all-around nice guy, he just happened to be in the same dance lesson classes with us 15 years earlier. We needed these lessons badly as, in addition to being wildly intelligent, caring and thoughtful, Tesa can not let someone else lead when dancing. So, we were taking lessons so that we wouldn't make fools of ourselves during our wedding dance, and Dr. Johnson was right there the whole time.

"So", I asked Tesa, "what happened at Dr. Johnson's that was so bad we had to switch to a new eye doctor?!"

I assumed he must have said something sexist, racist or insulted one of our children. Maybe he no longer took our insurance or the person at the front desk overcharged us and wouldn't credit the extra fees.

The answer was that Dr. Johnson did nothing. Another ophthalmologist did.

A new eye doctor, Dr. Clara, opened up 3 blocks from Dr. Johnson. Tesa, of course, heard about Dr. Clara from a good friend who mentioned that Dr. Clara did not dilate your eyes during the exam. Tesa hated getting those nasty drops that ruined the rest of her day; the burning sensation when having the drops, the blinding light shined into your newly sensitive eyes, squinting through sunglasses for hours and then not being able to look at a computer screen for half the day— I think everyone hates getting their eyes dilated. Maybe as much as they hate going to the dentist.

Dr. Clara, however, had invested in a machine that made the inconvenience of getting your eyes dilated unnecessary. I'm sure this machine was not inexpensive. Therefore, it made sense that care at Dr. Clara's office costs more. Additionally, her location was harder to get to, had worse parking and she was definitely not in our dancing class.

The clinical results of her machine are likely only equal to those of dilating your eyes with eye drops. So, from an eye doctor perspective, it was just a more expensive way to do the same thing.

But from Tesa's perspective it was more than enough reason to change doctors.

Bringing this story home to dentistry, we find that this type of experience is not unique to Tesa and our eye doctor. Other than relocations, the number one reason why people change dentists is that the practice does not offer what the patient wants.[5]

---

[5] Why do people change dentists (bad experience, insurance, etc.) January 24th, 2017. Contributors: Rakhee I., Sarah F., Kristen G

Just as Tesa was able to find out that Dr. Clara has new technology that makes our family visits more comfortable and convenient, your patients are relentlessly scouting for a better dental experience.

In today's reality, we are all distracted all the time and are constantly looking to satisfy our every whim. Just enter your break room at lunchtime and look at the caring, incredibly social professionals that you work with every day. Chances are there is very little conversation and everyone is scrolling mindlessly on their phones for the next bit of information, gizmo or experience that is going to make their life 0.01% better.

We live in a world where you can get anything you want instantly. I mean, almost literally, anything; from a computer to a car, you can have it delivered same-day and often within an hour. Yet we, in dentistry, expect our patients to not mind being greatly inconvenienced by how we deliver their care.

Here's the dirty little secret though; there are a few offices that cater to patients' desires and patients seek them out.

Just like Tesa, these patients also tell their friends and these practices grow at an exponential rate.

I became acutely aware of how much people are looking for a better dental experience when we launched our Therapeutic Virtual Reality (TVR) system, the Digital Nitrous.

There is over a decade of research proving the efficacy of TVR being as effective as a light narcotic at controlling anxiety and pain. Digital Nitrous is the first system to leverage this research to enhance the dental experience for both patients and caregivers.

The number one reasons why dentists love using TVR is because it saves them time. But, it is also a transformational dental experience for patients.

The very first time we used a prototype for Digital Nitrous, also called OperaVR, on a patient it was featured on the news. The news station heard about Digital Nitrous through a friend of mine that knew what I was working on, and who was so excited about it that she wanted to feature it on the evening news as soon as possible. Since then, it has been featured in dozens of magazines and local news stations, including being featured in CNN Business and in *O, The Oprah Magazine.*

I don't know a better mouth to get word-of-mouth referrals from than Oprah's.

When we first launched TVR, we were right next to the CBCT systems on the trade show floor. Digital Nitrous was 1.5% the cost of the cone beam.

If you make the conservative assumption that you would get one new patient a week through word of mouth referrals, at a value of $1000 per new patient, Digital Nitrous pays for itself in less than two weeks. And it should easily pay off that cone beam within two years.

This is just another example of an extremely valuable "coffee pot" that could be viewed as purely for the patients' benefit, but ends up providing massive value to the dental office and team.

When we advertise TVR directly to dentists, using phrases like "grow your practice", we consistently get scores of comments from patients clamoring for us to let their dentist know it is available. Yet, only a fraction of dentists take action and apply this game-changing technology (that is as effective as nitrous oxide at addressing dental anxiety) in their practice.

Simply put; Therapeutic Virtual Reality like Digital Nitrous is wildly effective at addressing patient anxiety and growing your practice. But, many dentists I talk to complain about having to "try out something new." They truly believe that dental anxiety is the patients' problem.

They are wrong.

Patient anxiety has been shown to delay dental treatment 22% of the time.[6] That means almost 1 in 4 dental treatments diagnosed get delayed due to dental anxiety, or never get treated. This, in turn, means your dental office production is reduced by 22%.

This is your problem, not your patients'.

Until Therapeutic Virtual Reality, or TVR, the only way to address patient anxiety in the dental chair was drugs. As mentioned, TVR sedation is similar to a light narcotic at reducing pain and anxiety, as the functional MRI image of the brain of a patient with a pain stimulus under the

---

[6] Oral Health and Well-Being in the United States. *Health Policy Institute State Fact Sheets,* 2015

influence of TVR looks similar to a patient with a pain stimulus under the influence of opioids[7-8].

What is at stake is simple:

Addressing patient needs, like conveniently controlling pain and anxiety, grows your practice through increased referrals and production.

On the other hand, if you don't take the time to focus on your patients' needs, you are absolutely leaving your practice vulnerable, and run the risk of causing your practice to wither or die.

To find out more about Therapeutic Virtual Reality and OperaVR the Digital Nitrous go to ThePatientFirstManifesto.com/Free

---

[7] Factors influencing the efficacy of virtual reality distraction analgesia during postburn physical therapy: preliminary results from 3 ongoing studies. Sam R Sharar, Gretchen J Carrougher, Dana Nakamura, Hunter G Hoffman, David K Blough, David R Patterson. *Arch Phys Med Rehabil.* 2007 Dec;88(12 Suppl 2):S43-9. doi:10.1016/j.apmr.2007.09.004.

[8] Using FMRI to study the neural correlates of virtual reality analgesia. Hunter G Hoffman, Todd L Richards, Aric R Bills, Trevor Van Oostrom, Jeff Magula, Eric J Seibel, Sam R Sharar. *CNS Spectr.* 2006 Jan;11(1):45-51. doi: 10.1017/s1092852900024202.

5.

The Importance of Going Paperless

*"You can have everything in life you want,
if you will just help enough other people
get what they want."*

Zig Ziglar

I BELIEVE THAT IGNORING THE PATIENTS' PERSPECTIVE and not implementing the small, easy conveniences patients are looking for is a primary reason why we live in the grim reality that many dentists today don't have enough extra profit to fund a retirement plan. Actually, very few dentists will be able to retire by age 60. In fact, the average age of retirement for a dentist in 2017 was 68.9, four years more than in 2001.[9] Meanwhile, the average age of retirement for the rest of the population is 62.[10]

I don't think dentists tend to retire later than others because we all love doing quadrants of posterior composites. I doubt most of us would rather be placing matrices in mouths at age 67 than playing with our grandchildren. Dentists just don't make and save enough money over the course of our careers.

Unfortunately, it is getting worse.

Dental benefit plans are paying less and less to dentists every year. Meanwhile the cost of equipment and supplies, as well as team wages, have skyrocketed. The rapidly dropping profitability of our practices has two massive implications on our future ability to retire EVER; we will make less and our practices will be worth less.

So, I urge you to look at your career as a timebomb. Not to say that it is a failure or about to explode, but instead that if you do not plan correctly there will be massive negative consequences. Every year, month, hour and minute in your practice, the fuse is burning. The time you have and the money you've saved for retirement adds up to the length of the fuse.

As you get older and save more, your fuse is shorter and the intensity to produce goes up. If you are younger, you may feel the false sense of security of time.

---

[9] Average Dentists Retires Later. *ADA Health Policy Institute* 08.20.2018.
[10] Chris Hogan. *Ramsey* (Online) 10.21.2020.

In either case, it is solely your ability to attract patients who trust you to address their dental needs that will either increase your ability to live comfortably throughout life or not.

The stakes could not be higher, but few dentists even realize that this is THE core issue holding their careers back. Additionally, even if most dentists knew exactly what to do to attract these patients, they would not take the most important step— action.

To drive this point home, I want to detail one simple process plaguing dental practices today and how to effectively act on the solution that will drive patients who trust you to deliver their care. The issue at hand is how you process new patient information.

If you are like approximately 80% of dental practices[11], you either have patients fill out paper forms in your office or have PDFs on your website for patients to download and bring in to their appointments. Both of these are unacceptable today.

A 2020 study that emerged just after the COVID-19 pandemic shutdown was over showed that 53% of patients said they would switch medical providers if it meant they could get access to touchless patient intake and registration tools.[12] This means more than half of all your patients would leave

---

[11] OperaDDS 2020 phone survey

[12] "2020 Healthcare Consumer Experience Study", Cedar, 2020.

your practice for a different practice if they find out that you do not use paperless forms, but the other practice does.

Yet, thousands upon thousands of offices still have not made the switch to paperless forms.

Patients expect us to be able to process their information, like privacy policies, consent forms, and new patient forms, like every other industry. We need the ability to easily text or email forms to patients so they can fill them out from any device, and have our forms available on our website for patients to fill out when it is convenient for them.

Not having your forms easily available is a sign to patients that you are outdated and that you do not care about their satisfaction or their needs.

The ability to process patient information through messaging and on your website isn't just for your patients' convenience, however. It is also incredibly productive for offices and prevents the spread of disease.

You become massively more productive because you streamline the process of having to collect information multiple times, every time you see a patient. You prevent the spread of disease because there are so many less touch points on surfaces that do not get adequately disinfected in most offices.

Let's examine the time savings you would achieve leveraging secure online information processing from the average patient visit:

First the appointment has to be scheduled. This can be done automatically online in a number of ways, saving your team the time of a phone call or email exchange. This adds up to a very conservative 3 minutes.

I won't even include in our calculation the over 5 minutes per patient you save using automated patient reminders, as most offices have a patient reminder system in place that is quite effective.

Before the appointment, you should be doing a medical pre-screening to make sure the patient is not sick prior to coming into the office. This should be done by the patient at home either from an automated message or on your website. This became necessary during the COVID-19 pandemic, but I believe this protocol should continue indefinitely.

Doing this simple step is not only saving your office from either losing production from having a sick team member or being the next epicenter of a pandemic outbreak, it saves your office 2 minutes of form intaking and processing.

Next, consider having the patient check in virtually. Removing the need for patients to stop at the front desk removes a huge bottleneck in processing every appointment, frees up crucial capacity at your front desk and will save you another 4 minutes.

During the appointment you have to update the medical history (2 minutes), obtain signed consent for whatever you are doing (2 minutes) and then make financial arrangements (2 minutes).

Paperless forms will, therefore, save you at least 15 minutes every time you see a patient. And this doesn't even include all the extra costs and time associated with the printing, processing, scanning and shredding of those pathogen transporting documents.

All the while creating a much better, more convenient way for your patients to receive higher quality care.

One of the great group practices we work with that has over 20 locations using paperless forms did the cost benefit analysis on using secure forms as I have described here and determined that they saved, on average, $2300 per month. They also stated that they did, indeed, save over 15 minutes per appointment of processing time.

If you only see twenty patients a day, that is 5 hours of your time and your team's time saved every day.

That's time you can obviously use to produce more high quality dentistry

Bottom line; if you aren't using online information collection from your patients, you are hurting your profits and inconveniencing everyone.

While paperless forms are an easy, simple example of how ignoring patients' expectations can end up hurting your practice, you can make the same case for major investments like 3D printing, CT imaging, or CAD/CAM same day crowns.

For the full roadmap of game changing dental technologies, implementation tips and breakdown of the results you can expect from successfully incorporating each technology go to ThePatientFirst-Manifesto.com/Free

6.

The New Measuring Stick

"So often in life things that you regard as an impediment turn out to be great, good fortune."

- Ruth Bader Ginsberg

IT WAS A SUNDAY MORNING DURING MY FIRST YEAR OUT of dental school when I went to Target to return a shirt that didn't fit. I was on my way to work out, so I had on my typical weekend outfit: cargo shorts, tee shirt and a baseball cap. I hadn't showered or shaved, but I didn't smell bad either.

At the counter, while the clerk was mindlessly scanning the item, a loud yelp came from my right. Both the clerk and I jumped in shock and turned to see the cause of the alarm in unison.

The woman who had just gasped looked at me with wide eyes, showing she was just as stunned as the two of us, and demanded, "Dr. Laskin, what are you doing here?!"

I curtly replied, "Well, I don't always wear a lab coat— sometimes I have to return stuff to Target, too."

As my (rightfully) offended patient of record slinked away, my mind was occupied with the audacity of someone who wouldn't realize that her dentist isn't always in the dental practice. Sometimes we walk around the city and do normal stuff, just like everyone else.

Well, as I look back at that interaction twenty years later, I realize that dentists do the same thing to their patients every day. We treat our patients like they do not have a life outside our offices.

From expecting people to not mind being inconvenienced by being rescheduled because we are running late, to having people come in for short evaluations that could have been handled with a secure image being sent to us via teledentistry, we consistently act like our patients' time is insignificant.

Every doctor can likely identify with me when I say that if you ask me about a patient by name, I likely will not know him or her. Tell me their hobbies and I will just look at you like you are speaking a foreign language. But, if you tell me the dentistry I performed in their mouth, I will quickly know exactly who you are talking about.

This is just further evidence that we often exclusively focus on people's dentition at the cost of ignoring almost everything else.

A simple exercise will show you how much we in dentistry ignore what goes on in the rest of the world while our patients, who are just normal people that have lives outside of our offices, continue to have experiences that they will negatively compare us to:

1. Make a reservation and have dinner at a random restaurant and list all the details, positive and negative about the experience.
2. Make a reservation and have your teeth cleaned at a random dental practice and jot down all those experiences.
3. Finally, compare the two lists.

If your list is anything like mine, it will include major gaps in how the dental experience compares. The restaurant had online reservation scheduling versus being told to arrive at the dental office 15 minutes before the actual appointment to complete my paperwork.

I was greeted by a friendly, smiling person who instructed me to get a drink at the bar at the restaurant while I waited to be seated. When I entered the dental practice, a team member slid a clipboard to me and pointed at it while grunting to the phone in her ear.

At dinner, I was escorted to the well decorated table and carefully presented a menu. For my cleaning, I was escorted to a room filled with gangly hoses and unorganized dental supplies, then a cold metal bib chain was draped over my neck.

This is the comparison that your patients are making today.

The new measuring stick for dentistry is not the dental office across the street. It is every experience that the patient has with every business transaction as they walk around planet Earth.

What other industry relies on the phone as its main form of communication? Phones aren't even used to make calls to people's friends anymore, let alone businesses. Yet many dental offices force patients to use this outdated technology as their only form of communication.

Believe it or not, dental offices are even behind the times compared to auto body shops.

About five years ago, I backed into a hygienist's car in our parking lot and had to get both cars repaired. *Great, I thought to myself, when am I going to even find the time to get multiple estimates for this, let alone get the work done?*

Turns out, I could snap a few quick pictures and get an estimate in hours. We created the same functionality, tri-aging emergencies through teledentistry forms, less than a year later.

However, it took a global pandemic that shut down offices, making it physically impossible for patients to come into practices for two full months across the entire country, before most dentists paid any attention to the technology called teledentistry.

Now, as the saying goes, that toothpaste is out of the tube and there is no putting it back in.

Patients now know what technologies, processes and procedures we have available today and they don't just talk to each other about it. They post reviews and comments online and spread news, good or bad, at an increasing rate. Their pleas for us to change are growing at a similar rate, but most dentists are ignoring their cries.

These dentists will be left behind by those of us who refuse to accept that we can't do better. Many practices will go the way of AOL, Kodak, Sears and Kmart.

These apathetic dentists can not be our benchmark. For dentistry to continue to exist as the great profession it is today and for our practices to thrive, our new benchmark must be world-class companies like Apple, Disney, Starbucks and Nordstrom.

It doesn't take a specialist in retail to understand why Kmart is dying and Target thrives. A quick walk through the stores will enlighten you to the causes of one company's growth and another's decline. Just pull up the websites, give them a call or buy something. This is what our patients are doing to us every day and there are far more differences in our practices than there are between retail chains.

It is actually easy to ascertain the steps needed to address these patient needs and desires. All it takes is looking at your office with a critical eye as if it were not your own, while keeping in mind what you know about other industries and other dental practices.

Similarly, I would recommend you hire someone you know who has never been to your practice for half a day to look at every detail of your practice with "fresh eyes". Have them make a list of everything **negative** they can. Starting off with the initial phone call or online forms, to the parking lot and exterior of your building, even assessing how easy it is for them to leave you a glowing review on Facebook.

I must, however, warn you; reading this feedback will hurt.

The list will be long and seem petty. Every paint chip should be documented; every whisper they hear your team make about lunch needs to be captured; every single annoying inconvenience they think could be improved even a little bit will seem like an attack on the quality of care your team provides.

But, it will also be an incredible empowering list to keep that you can use to plan from.

You will see what patients care about and some of these issues will be very easy to address. Dusting paintings, getting the food wrappers cleaned up out of your parking lot and making your patient reminder message more clear should just take your team minutes.

Other items may take longer, or cost too much to address right away, but at least you will know what your patients are thinking and not telling you. You can then make the change when the time is right for you.

I would recommend doing this exercise annually. In between the annual exercise, you can capture feedback by automating your patient reviews to be sent after every encounter. These reviews should ask the simple question, "How can we improve?" and include a button that says,

"Inform Management" so the patient knows that this is internal feedback used for improvements and not shown on social media for others to see.

Automating reviews in this way, your best patients will give you the feedback they want, while still being able to give you a positive review on social media. Most patients that have had a negative experience just want to be able to easily let you know their feedback.

In other words, patients, like all people, just want to be heard.

Therefore, giving this easy option for patients to give you important feedback will also diffuse the desire for people to post negative reviews about their experiences online.

When we turned on this functionality in OperaDDS, we received over ten times the review volume at my practice. That is ten times more positive reviews on social media and ten times more feedback internally.

The feedback from these reviews have been instrumental in allowing us to continue to improve patients' experiences and keep generating referrals over and over again.

7.

Leadership, Management and Doctors

"Talent wins games, but teamwork and intelligence win championships."

Michael Jordan

MANY PEOPLE STRUGGLE WITH CONTROLLING THEIR weight, as I certainly have.

However, losing weight should be so easy. All you need to do is eat less and exercise more. Yet, somehow I, along with millions and millions of people, continue to flounder to control the size of my midsection several times a year.

It is a classic struggle which I believe is a great metaphor for what is happening in dental offices around the country right now. Both the formula to lose weight and the formula to grow your practice is simple to understand in theory but, in reality, it is actually monumentally hard to execute.

Another commonality in both dilemmas lies in the fact that both weightloss and practice profitability rely on two primary factors, yet most of us focus on the least important of these principles to try and accomplish our goals.

As previously mentioned, in the case of losing weight, the two factors are how many calories you consume (eating) and how many calories you burn (exercise). Like a lot of people, I actually enjoy working out hard, even for long lengths of time. I have a home gym that I wake up and use consistently at 5:45 every morning. At least five days a week I am left breathless and sweaty after exerting 100% of my effort in free weights, treadmill running, elliptical training and stationary biking.

So, if pain makes progress, I should be cut like a Hemsworth, right?!

But, I also love eating pizza and drinking wine.

Therein lies my problem; while working out is key to being healthy, I've found that I'd have to workout 4 hours a day with the intensity of Michael Phelps getting ready to win his next medal in order to keep up with how much I love eating.

Given my schedule, this just isn't feasible; even if I had the time, I would likely end up in the hospital with major injuries by the time I hit my goals. So, for me to control my weight, I must control how much I eat, no matter how much I work out. It is a painful truth that has taken me about a decade to (kind of) come to grips with.

In the case of growing our dental practices, dentists know that in order to have a healthy practice, they must deliver high quality dental care. Therefore, dental professionals commonly focus on training their dental skills with great intensity.

The complexity and detail required to achieve clinical success demands that we focus on elevating our skills in order to not have failures. And we *feel* every failure intensely. These normal but catastrophic realities of being a dental professional berate our daily life to the point of requiring our obsessive attention to detail.

We often leave the office at the end of the day as if we just ended a workout session, exhausted but feeling like we worked so hard that our success is all but guaranteed.

But, just as working out makes me feel like I immediately lost 10 pounds (up to the point I step on a scale), performing quality clinical care is actually a small part of the success equation. The clinical care you deliver doesn't really get you closer to your profitability goals or move your business metrics appreciably at all.

So, just as there are millions of active Americans whose diet has led to them being obese, the lack of attention to our consumer, the patient, has led to overworked doctors who are falling behind financially.

At the turn of the century, the average dentist made about twice the income of their family of origin. This, coupled with an industry that averaged 4 days of work with "banker's hours", meant dentists (including myself) were fat and happy. The motivation to change was low.

Why mess with success, right? Predictably, most of us didn't. This has led to many dental offices not looking any different than they did in the year 2000.

I would ask you to make a list of what substantial changes you have made in your practice in the last twenty years. However, only keep the changes on this list that patients would notice. Strive to look only for items on the list that patients would notice from the viewpoint of what has happened to the rest of their world in that time frame.

For context, think of how Wikipedia (2001), the iPod (2003), Facebook (2004), YouTube (2005), and the iPhone (2007) were all released in the early 2000s. Mobile phones existed but didn't have cameras until the year 2000. Now in dentistry we have Therapeutic Virtual Reality (TVR), artificial intelligence writing chart notes and reading X-rays, CAD/CAM, CT imaging, touchless form processing and teledentistry. But what percentage of dentists have incorporated these technologies? Nothing like the way consumers have gobbled up YouTube and iPhones.

What does this mean? Dentists, and healthcare in general, have been slow to adopt technologies that every person expects to use on a daily basis; simple technologies like online check-in and paperless payment processing. We, in healthcare, cling to dying technology like no other industry.

It isn't a mystery what led to this dilemma. Dentists have to be psychologists, architects, artists, scientists and engineers, all while leading a team, running a business and being the main producer. Back in the mid-1990s, when I went to dental school, balancing these job duties was not too difficult. The profitability of delivering care allowed dentists to either spend their downtime working on business tasks or pay consultants to help fill gaps in their abilities.

The training for dentists has been, meanwhile, inadequate for what the job entails. But this is not the fault of dental educators either. The information and skills development required to produce dentists that know how to provide quality care is a full time, four year job.

It is commonly said that "dentists are bad business people"; I believe that this is blatantly false. Almost everyone is bad at business, not just dentists.

The major difference between most business owners and doctors is that we have about twelve other jobs we need to focus on, in addition to running the business.

Additionally, there are so many individual skill sets in dentistry that commonly get lumped together under the broad category of "business": sales, marketing, operations, accounting, facility management, human resources— the list goes on and on. No business the size of the average dental practice would likely rely on the highest producer, the rain-maker, to handle all these tasks, let alone expect them to excel at any one of them.

Furthermore, we have the two "big boss duties" that every doctor must do to some degree: leadership and management. While leadership and management are often mistakenly used synonymously, I believe it is crucial to note that leadership and management are unrelated competencies.

I define leadership as setting the vision for your endeavor or business and constantly communicating that vision to everyone. The goal of quality leadership is, therefore, to ensure everyone on the team is aligned on where you, collectively, are headed.

Management, on the other hand, is delegating tasks to people and removing any barriers that may hinder their ability to complete those tasks. The objective for management, then, is to clearly define everyone's role in obtaining the vision for your business, as well as holding everyone accountable to the part that each person has agreed to play in pursuing your collective goals.

It is important to note that when describing all these separate business, leadership and management capabilities, there is no skill that would even remotely translate to what most doctors almost exclusively focus on: clinical care.

It is, therefore, vitally important to understand how to handle leadership and management in your practice. While doctors are, by nature of the position, leaders and managers of the clinical team, they are not required to lead or manage the overall business.

Leadership and management duties can easily be delegated to others, who may have a more natural affinity for them, or at least have the extra capacity in their job to handle these tasks more effectively.

If you are leading or managing the business beyond the clinical aspects of care, I would highly recommend taking an adjective inventory of your leadership and management skills and adjusting the duties in your office appropriately.

Given that leading and managing others are skills that can be learned, you can either obtain the knowledge required to achieve your goals, or delegate these responsibilities to others. If you are looking to delegate these tasks, you can either look for members of your team to delegate to, look for outside resources or even look for a transition in your practice where others could assist in running the day-to-day operations more effectively.

To learn how to take inventory of everyone on you team's skills, along with how to lead, manage and delegate effectively go to ThePatientFirstManifesto.com/Free

8.

Your Limiting Belief

*"Understand your limitations
and capitalize on them."*

—Bruce Lee

IN THE SPIRIT OF FULL TRANSPARENCY, I MUST ADMIT
that when I graduated from dental school in 1999, I felt
barely equipped to see patients.

Each time I entered an operatory, I felt like a mouse getting dropped into a snake pit (and likely looked like it). As
a result of my insecurities, I spent almost all my spare time
focused on improving my clinical skills.

I was actually relatively adept at producing above average
clinical dentistry, but dental school had ground what little
self confidence I entered my education with into dust by
graduation day. I think all dentists have stories from dental

school that illustrate their dental education resembling more of a boot camp than a constructive learning experience.

Here is one of my experiences from my first few months of dental school that directly led to my being obsessed for a decade with clinical quality, yet maintained little confidence in my ability to deliver it:

It was my first graded project in Operative Dentistry. The job was simple, create a full crown wax pattern on a model of a preparation we were given for tooth #19.

For those who did not have to wax in dental school, historically, wax patterns were used to pattern, invest and cast gold in order to make dental restorations, like crowns, prior to the advancements in CAD/CAM dentistry.

And for this entomology major from Madison, waxing was hard. Hair-pulling, instrument throwing, why-did-I-go-to-dental-school hard.

Luckily for me, I had a lifeline. At the University of Minnesota Dental School, every freshman dental student is paired up with a sophomore to be their mentor. My mentor was Kevin, a great guy who shared my passion for playing music. We hit it off instantly.

In addition to being a friend, Kevin was also a great mentor who lived at the dental school fraternity close by campus, making his help easily accessible whenever I needed it. In this case, I obviously needed his help.

Beyond being conveniently located and enjoyable to be around, Kevin was so proficient at waxing restorations that the dental school professors gave him the nickname "The Wax God".

My path to success for this assignment was clear. I took 20 minutes, slapped some wax on the model that represented a potato more than a tooth, and headed over to meet Kevin so he could work his magic and show me how a master works his craft.

Over the next few hours, Kevin patiently instructed me on the nuances of crown waxing and anatomy of the lower left first mandibular molar. I was an attentive, focused, yet horribly unskilled student. After over three hours of work, my lack of waxing ability finally became too much for even Kevin to bear, when he pushed me aside and finally got to work demonstrating his techniques.

About an hour later, I left the fraternity with a supermodel #19 crown sculpted in dental wax. I doubt there was one molecule of wax that was in the same position that I had placed it when Kevin was done.

The Wax God had created another masterpiece, and I was going to present this one to the bench instructor as my own design. My only anxiety with this assignment, therefore, came from the simple fact that the perfection of this pattern clearly showed that I had not waxed this crown, so it was quite likely that I would be questioned about how I, the sloppy freshman, had produced something of such beauty.

The next day I walked to dental school with this jewel of Kevin's handiwork literally placed in a ring box on a square piece of felt. God forbid I should bump and mar this vision *of excellence, I would never be able to make it look anything like what The Wax God had created.*

The first two hours of school went by slowly that day, as I eagerly awaited presenting the piece of art to my bench instructor, Ivan. When the time finally arrived, I presented the triumph of #19 wax to Ivan beaming with pride. "Yes, this is what I have to offer you today. Admire its brilliance!", I thought to myself while Ivan wordlessly inspected Kevin's work.

It took Ivan about ten minutes to closely inspect the pattern under high magnification and jot his little notes down on the evaluation sheet. I was sure not to look, as I didn't want to spoil the pleasant comments Ivan was about to reveal.

Ivan slid my evaluation paper across the desk and turned it around to unveil some check marks and notes, but my eye was drawn only to the grade which was written in large numbers:

3.2 / 10

What followed was four years of similar soul-crushing experiences aimed, I believe, to instill the fear of being a hack dentist, who is a danger to society, into my every waking thought.

It worked.

Ivan and his comrades were fantastic clinicians. They were masters at tooth preparations and could create amazing dental restorations. But I don't think any of my bench instructors had much business success in their dental careers.

For example, the dentist that taught me the interesting-but-now-useless art of setting denture teeth sold real estate. He often told me stories about how his dental practice failed due to his hatred of seeing patients.

Looking back on it now, I believe that the anxiety that was poured into me during dental school was a gift. Not for the outcome of obsessing over the quality of care that my instructors were expecting, however.

Instead, my anxiety landed mainly on my questioning my own ability to succeed in producing a decent income through a career in dentistry. Like many dentists, I entered dental school thinking that one of the major benefits of being a doctor of dental surgery was a comfortable income. I had been told by everyone outside of dental school that if I ran my own office, I would be set.

In school I saw a very different reality, however. I heard tale after tale about the challenges of managing teams and how much patients hate going to the dentist. I also saw, for the first time, dentists who had failed to make a living seeing patients.

This freaked me out! I had never had a filling or ortho-dontics, so I knew absolutely nothing about dentistry when entering school and I knew even less about business.

I thought owning a dental practice was like owning a slot machine that paid off with every pull. The dentists I met in dental school told me the truth; running a practice is hard. Mentally and financially oppressive, in fact.

Armed with this fear coming out of school, I spent tremendous amounts of time and energy learning about business early in my career. I wish I could say my curiosity was fueled by a desire for success, but it was definitely more fueled by my thinking that I was sure to fail.

It took me two full years after dental school to gain the gumption to buy my first dental office. I bought the smallest office I could find, so my bank loan would be as low as possible thinking that I would then be less likely to default.

During the first two years of practice ownership, I speed-read every issue of every dental magazine about dental economics and all the best business books I could. I studied business and practice management more intensely than I did clinical dentistry in school, because it felt like the stakes were just as high.

Through my studies, I learned a simple, dirty little secret:

Running a successful dental practice has almost nothing to do with the quality of care you deliver.

This fact does not make me (and likely you) happy, but it is nevertheless true. You can try to skirt the issue by asking, "how do you define success?", but I would argue that a successful dental practice must check many proverbial boxes. Surely one of these checkmarks for success of practice includes high quality care.

But one of those boxes must also include solid financials. And high quality of care has very little to do with profit or even patient satisfaction.

We all know doctors who have incredibly successful growing practices, filled with patients who receive below average dental care. We also know phenomenal clinicians who barely hang on to their practice, or end up selling it at a massive discount just to get out of a financial hole that they have dug themselves into.

Obviously, you can not hurt people, do horrible work and expect your practice to succeed. But, you also do not need to be even above average at delivering care to have a financially successful career.

Just like an untrained ear can not tell the difference between slightly off-pitch and perfect pitch, patients just can't tell the difference between excellent and average dental care. This is likely why almost every post of mediocre dentistry on dental forums ends with the line, "but the patient was happy".

Ignorance is bliss.

I have purchased practices from three phenomenal dentists for pennies on the dollar. The clinical quality produced in these practices was phenomenal. All three dentists had extremely high standards and had graduated from the best post-graduate dental education programs available.

Their standards of oral care were so high, in fact, that only their close friends and family shared them. They were amazing dentists (artists, really), but their failing practices led to shockingly low valuations. This is a common tragic final outcome of too many doctors' careers.

For example, some doctors are left with too little money to retire comfortably and are forced to work well beyond when they would like to stop. Some of these dentists develop health issues, yet still feel the financial burden to produce.

Many of these doctors are too embarrassed to share their stories, which is unfortunate as these stories could serve as a warning to their younger colleagues. It is all too common to see younger doctors driving BMWs or Mercedes that also do not contribute to a retirement fund.

That shiny car that represents success and quality is attractive to many of us, but the allure of what we want to see in our purchase is only a distortion of reality. Owning an expensive car does not mean you are successful.

Cars, houses and other expensive luxury items are little more than illusions that detract from financial independence, which is actually a quantifiable, definitive aspect of a successful career.

I am certainly not saying to not enjoy whatever success you obtain in your career. I am merely stating that there is a significant issue with the finances of many doctors that is too often swept under the rug. The only way to address this effectively is to discuss the problem and possible solutions openly.

Similarly, having your office's attention exclusively focused on high quality care alone isn't what it means to put patients first. We became dental professionals to elevate care. Quality care is more important to us than to our patients, or at least it should be.

Putting patients first means incorporating technology and procedures that directly address issues that your patients care about **in addition** to what we would like to focus on.

While both are important, I believe you can never go wrong if you put your patients' needs first.

Putting patients first means catering to our patients' needs and desires above our own.

9.

The Mindset Shift

"If you want others to be happy, practice compassion.
If you want to be happy, practice compassion."

- Dalai Lama

There is an old fable about two monks; one young and strong, one old and feeble. One day the two monks were taking their daily walk in silence through the forest, when they came upon a fellow monk who was trapped under a tree that had fallen on his leg.

The incapacitated monk was wriggling in obvious pain, with tears streaming down his face. The young monk, full of empathy, dropped to his knees shouting and straining to pull his fallen brother out from under the tree. The young monk's hard pulling on the poor man just seemed to exacerbate the injury, sending both monks into further distress.

Calmly, the old monk placed his hand on the shoulder of his young friend and firmly nodded to him with a glance that cut through his panic, causing the young monk to move out of the way. The elder then grabbed a nearby log and boulder, with which he created a fulcrum to lift the fallen tree off their pinned comrade. The young monk was then safely able to help their friend.

After they returned to the monastery and saw that their injured friend was being well tended to, the two monks sat down for tea.

"I am certainly strong enough that I could have easily lifted the tree, yet I was useless in helping our friend. So, why is it that you, who are so much older and not nearly as strong, were able to help today?" asked the young monk.

"That is simple, my brother," replied the wise monk. "You are such a caring person, who loves your brother intensely. Your admirable empathy for your fallen friend meant that you absorbed his own pain as your own, debilitating your reasoning. I, on the other hand, felt compassion for you both and the situation, but did not absorb either of your sufferings personally. So, I was able to assess the situation and respond caringly, but calmly and rationally in order to help you both."

I believe that this story accurately describes both the biggest problem in our delivery of care, as well as guides us to the solution. In order to understand this, allow me to present these three definitions:

1. *Empathy* is the ability to understand and share the feelings of another and vicariously experience their feelings.

2. *Apathy* is the lack of emotion or concern.
3. *Compassion* can be defined as sympathetic pity and concern for the sufferings or misfortunes of others.

Empathy, at first glance, seems like the benchmark we should all shoot for. Empathetic doctor or care team members are universally loved by patients and co-workers. If we share in our patients' hardships, we are acutely aware of their problems and perceive the best way to address their concerns.

The trouble with being an empathetic caregiver, and being an empathetic doctor who performs microsurgery all day specifically, is that the process of absorbing our patients' anxieties diminishes our ability to produce the high quality clinical outcomes we are all striving for.

Just as the younger monk **internalizing** the feelings of pain shared with his trapped friend left him ineffective, sharing our patients pain and anxiety can hobble our abilities to perform at our best.

Adding to the problem we face in providing care for people is the fact that, while sharing in other's pain is natural for most people, it is certainly enhanced in people who choose caregiving professions.

Caring for people and relieving their pain is a primary reason why so many of us became doctors and team members in the first place!

The shared suffering, however, drastically diminishes our efficacy, just as the young monk was rendered useless to his friend.

However, any patient or responsible caregiver will immediately understand that apathy toward patients is not commendable or even acceptable. We, doctors and team members, must maintain concern for our patients in order to appropriately address their needs.

Not having emotion or caring for our patients, obviously, is not the goal.

So we are left with the dilemma:

If we treat our patients with empathy, our quality of care will drop, as we will be disabled through absorbing their anxieties.

If we treat our patients with apathy, our quality will drop because of our disinterest. Also, nobody wants an apathetic doctor, so your practices would likely fail.

Of course, then, the answer lies in our first fully understanding the factors at play in this dilemma, and addressing them through exercising compassion in our delivery of care.

If we can treat patients from a place of compassion, we can both elevate our quality of care and maintain our human connection with patients by working to protect our own emotions as we focus on our detailed work.

Everything we do in a dental office, from a routine cleaning to root canals and extractions, requires a level of precision that would benefit from practicing conscious compassion toward our patients.

This does not happen by accident, however. Treating patients with true compassion requires recognition of this issue and consistent practice. But, by consistently making the mindful leveraging of restrained emotions a priority in our delivery of care, we can obtain the positive clinical outcomes we are looking for, while also addressing the needs of those anxious people who are commonly receiving this care.

Many times dentists joke that the "problem" that chokes our practice growth, slows us down, and hinders our ability to provide high quality care lies 6 inches above where we work—in our patients' minds. If only patients knew what we knew, would listen to what we say, would stop complaining about costs, pain and stress of treatment, sit still and relax, we could get our job done well.

This myopic perspective does not help anyone, including the doctor or caregiver.

I would argue that the primary factor stifling offices from hitting their goals in generating massive profits and helping more patients elevate their oral health lies in a different location than the patients' mind.

I believe the biggest limitation on professionals in our industry reaching their goals lies deeper— in our hearts.

Dental professionals are caring, nurturing empathetic creatures by nature. The number one question I get when people find out that I am a dentist is, "why would you want to dig around in other people's mouths?" We all endure these types of questions, but to us the answer is clear.

We want to help people.

The oral cavity is the gateway to health and we are the gatekeepers. Sure the money has historically been good, but there are certainly easier ways to make similar money and many more ways to make more with much less stress.

We must, therefore, recognize that the stress in our jobs is squarely derived from our empathy. The vast majority of the people we see have anxiety about coming to the dentist! We absorb that anxiety every hour, every patient, every day.

Yet, in this stressful environment, we are expected to perform micro-surgeries, where perfection is expected to the nanometer.

I can clearly remember walking into an operation last week thinking, *if the patient would stop crying, this filling will take less than 90 seconds.* Every day, a "simple" procedure that we have easily accomplished thousands of times is made extremely difficult by the person who those teeth are connected to.

The reason why this is so difficult is because we care.

But, over time we become desensitized to the suffering of our patients in order to perform our job effectively. This typically is not through mindful compassion, but through self preservation. In other words, we subconsciously ignore our patients' feelings, so that our own empathic nature doesn't impede us from delivering quality care.

Yet, ultimately, patients just want to know that you care.

Caring too much incapacitates us like the young monk in the fable. We must, however, understand what our patients need while also maintaining our focus so that we can produce the highest quality of care we can.

We must become like the old monk. Through consistent practice, doctors and care professionals can do the work necessary to act on their patients' desires for a less stressful, high quality, more compassionate dental experience, while also producing great work.

It only takes two steps to cross the chasm of The Great Disconnect between doctors and teams and their patients, so that you can achieve a practice beyond your dreams:

1. Learn what patients want
2. Take action

There is no doubt that, for most, the second step is the hardest. Implementing change can be difficult for practices and teams, so it is important to have a plan of action with each initiative you take on.

We all have seen an opportunity to improve care and failed to implement the solution successfully. For every hundred successful CAD/CAM systems out there cranking out dozens of cost-saving, well-fitting, beautiful restorations every day in dental practices, there is a number that sit in a closet collecting dust.

The difference between being successful in implementing a new technology or procedure in your practice lies in making sure that you fully understand the core issue you are trying to solve and setting a distinct implementation plan in place.

For more information on how to implement any change into your practice, including the ten part Implementation Checklist, go to ThePatientFirstManifesto.com/Free

10.

Pain

"The pain of yesterday is the strength of today."
—Paulo Coelho

MERRIEM-WEBSTER'S DICTIONARY DEFINES PAIN AS:

a localized or generalized unpleasant bodily sensation or complex of sensations that causes mild to severe physical discomfort and emotional distress and typically results from bodily disorder (such as injury or disease).

It goes on to define pain as *a basic bodily sensation that is induced by a noxious stimulus, is received by naked nerve endings, is associated with actual or potential tissue damage, is characterized by physical discomfort (such as pricking, throbbing, or aching), and typically leads to evasive action.*

My favorite of the three definitions the dictionary provides, however, is the last one: *One that irks or annoys or is otherwise troublesome.*

The reason why this last definition is my favorite is that it clearly states how annoying pain is in dentistry; both for the patient and for the doctor.

In the case of patients, dentistry has long been deemed synonymous with pain. Horror movies, comedians and musicals have all illustrated this point effectively. Detailing the numerous popular TV, movie scenes and comedy routines is likely unnecessary here, as it is obvious that dentistry and pain have been linked for far too long.

For doctors and care team members, pain is the greatest barrier and stress producer we have to deal with on a daily basis. If we could manage pain successfully, we could produce amazing clinical results much faster. Anyone who has worked on sedated patients knows how much easier, efficient and more profitable it can be working on patients that don't fear or feel pain.

Even so, pain is not necessary for patients to perceive it in the vast majority of cases we see in dentistry today. We have new, improved needles and anesthetics, both topical and local, that provide vastly more profound anesthesia easily, to the point where anything more than mild physical discomfort can be completely avoided.

Yet, contrary to the throngs of dentists who claim to be "painless", the belief that going to the dentist equates to undergoing painful procedures endures.

I think there are two main reasons for this:

1. Dentists do not truly understand the value of pain management
2. The persistence of patient anxiety

While in dental school, I read the book *Multi-million Dollar Dental Practice* by Dr. Mike Kesner. What stood out to me was the simple idea that nothing can help your practice more than the ability to give a painless injection. As a result, one of the only "A's" I received while in dental school was in the course Pain Management. Since then, I have had the opportunity to work with Dr. Kesner and thank him in person.

I've also expanded on his work into courses where I train others in the art of painless injections.

If you are not convinced that reducing your patients' pain is essential to growing your practice and you ignore their discomfort, you are, by definition, hurting people. People do not repeatedly go back to businesses that hurt them.

Think about it this way; nobody would go back to a restaurant where every meal came with the requirement to be slapped by the waiter.

But, even if you master the skill of pain management, removing negative sensation is not enough to grow your practice, as patient anxiety would allow the perception of pain to persist. To understand this, let us first explore the crucial association between pain and anxiety.

If you graph pain sensitization, where the vertical y-axis measures pain intensity and the x-axis measures stimulus intensity, you would see that the pain response follows an s-curve. (see fig. 1)

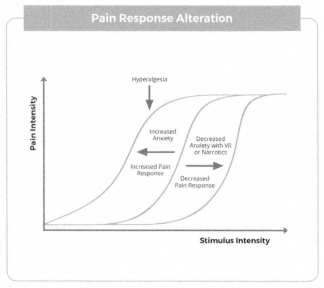

Fig. 1

The position of this s-curve, however, can be influenced by several factors, such as anxiety.

As anxiety increases, the pain response s-curve shifts to the left, thereby requiring less stimulus to elicit a pain response. Conversely, as anxiety decreases, it requires more stimulus to get a pain response.

The positive shifting of the s-curve to the right of the pain scale in response to lowering stress is why anxiolytics, such as nitrous oxide, triazolam and Therapeutic VR, like Digital Nitrous, work so well to reduce dental patients' anxiety. When patients are relaxed, they do not feel pain unless we hurt them.

This phenomenon also explains why anxious patients seem to feel everything. The shifting of the pain response to the left makes it so it requires very little stimulation to invoke a response.

This leads to much frustration for both dental professionals and patients and is the reason why we will not be able to transform people's opinion of dentistry being painful until we directly address their anxiety.

Doctors, however, will continue to fail to address patient anxiety until we are able to view dentistry through their eyes.

For reference, let's simply explore the most common dental idioms. These include, "by the skin of one's teeth", "armed to the teeth" and "cut your teeth".

However, no dental idiom is more popular than stating that something difficult "is worse than pulling teeth". This phrase is used by patients and doctors alike.

The fact that this saying is not, "it is worse than having your teeth pulled", illustrates that even our colloquialisms are biased toward the doctors' perspective.

Patients have no idea how hard it is to pull teeth. Yet, for dentists, pulling teeth really isn't that hard. It's just part of our job, which is made more difficult by our patients' anxiety, just like every other procedure we do.

If we look at the origin of the word *pain*, we see it comes from the Old French term *peine*, which refers to legal punishment or judgement. I think this is quite accurate for dentistry, as our patients judge us through our ability to positively or negatively control their pain.

Therefore, controlling pain for our patients is a fundamental key to growing our practices. As stated above, we can also see that the easiest way to control pain in your practice is by reducing patients' anxiety.

This mindshift to directly address our patients' pain through addressing their anxiety may seem simplistic and obvious. Through talking to doctors all around the country, however, I can assure you that there is only a small percentage who truly understand the power in addressing patient anxiety, and even less are aware of how much this stress is affecting their practice.

Even more important to the financial health of our practice is the health of our team members. Certainly reducing the pain that our patients feel in turn reduces the stress that we and our team feels. As explored in the previous chapter, we are empathetic care givers that absorb the discomfort of our patients, so it makes empirical sense that as our patients become more stressed, our team is more stressed too.

There is even considerable documentation reporting evidence that a dental practitioner's physical stress mirrors that of the patient's response during dental procedures. This includes higher blood pressure, increased heart rate and sweating.

I would suspect that everyone in dentistry has felt this and can point to dozens of patients that send their pulse skyrocketing as soon as they enter the room.

This has led to some devastating consequences for dental team members. It is commonly known that dentists have higher rates of suicide than the general poulation. Many dentists retire from practice early due to stress related disorders.[13]

In addition to the stress dentists receive from the physical delivery of care, dentists also report financial stress, business problems and feelings of time pressure.[14-15-16]

All of this stress can lead to burnout, substance abuse and cardiovascular stress.

So, in order to thoroughly reduce the stress that doctors and team members feel from the practice of dentistry, we must also address our business pressures of money and time, while also working diligently to minimize our patients' anxiety.

The most effective way I have found to increase production, case acceptance and fabricate time in a dental practice is through immediate, asynchronous team chat to increase Same Day Services in your practice.

---

[13] Freeman R, Main J R R, Burke F J T. Occupational stress and dentistry: Theory and practice. Part I Recognition. *Br Dent J* 1995; 178: 214-217

[14] Cooper C L, Watts J, Kelly M. Job satisfaction, mental health and job stressors among general dental practitioners in the UK. *Br Dent J* 1987; 162: 77-81

[15] Wilson R F, Coward PY, Capewell I et al. Perceived sources of occupational stress in general dental practitioners. *Br Dent J* 1998; 184: 499-502

[16] Newton J T, Gibbons D E. Stress in dental practice: A qualitative comparison of dentists working within the NHS and those working within an independent capitation scheme. *Br Dent J* 1996; 180: 329-334

11.

The Power of Same Day

*"The strength of the team is each individual member.
The strength of each member is the team."*

—Phil Jackson

MY VICE OF CHOICE IS COFFEE. I COULD GIVE UP EVERY other bad habit before I could give up coffee. I'd like to say it is because I just love it so much, but it would be more accurate to call this infatuation a caffeine addiction.

Twice I have tried to stop drinking coffee, thinking that I would be healthier and more focused. Both times I tried, I had multiple team members call my wife and beg her to tell me to go back to my caffeinated overlord.

So, when a Starbucks opened up in the same parking lot as my office a few years ago, I knew I was doomed. I usually go there several times a week and enjoy a tall black Pike

Place coffee to relax and do some work outside the office between patients.

You would think that I, like most dentists, can not leave the office too often, as I could miss out on an emergency case that walks in the door or people would need me at a moment's notice.

Thankfully, our cloud-based secure messaging system, Chat, makes it easy for me to get secure messages sent to me from the office anywhere, instantly. This frees me up to leave the physical walls of the practice without losing the ability for my team to communicate with me whenever they need me.

Seamless communication is the key to having a well coordinated team. As there was not an adequate system available on the market to handle my care team's communication, this was the first technology that I personally developed to upgrade my practice.

The reason why I felt so strongly that my office needed instant, secure messaging that is available anywhere is the simple fact that a well-coordinated team is perceived by patients as a competent team.

Furthermore, patients obviously want their care completed by a competent care team. So, it makes sense that instantaneous, complete communication between your team members is the best way to increase your patients' confidence in your care, thereby skyrocketing your case acceptance and production.

So, sometimes while I am sipping my coffee in the store surrounded by the smell of roasted beans, I get a slight vibration on my wrist from my Apple Watch notifying me that the practice needs something.

One recent memorable secure Chat message I received from a hygienist in my office read:

> **Sally at Operatory 1**
> **To:** *Dr. Laskin*
> **Patient:** *Bob Johnson*
> **Notes:** *Dr. Lane did the exam, but does not have time in her schedule to do treatment today. Bob would like to stay, so we moved him into room 6. I'll give him some anesthetic now.*
> **MedHx:** *no changes*
> **CC:** *broken #12 with caries*
> **Perio:** *mild gingivitis*
> **Restorative:** *Dr. Lane diagnosed #12 for a root canal and crown*
> **Images:** *PA and CBCT Scan*

This simple checklist message gives me all the information I need to know about Bob's exam in less than 10 seconds. It also let me know that I should get my butt back to the office and get to work.

Less than five minutes later I walked into the operatory where Bob was completely numb and relaxed under Digital Nitrous sedation. We were able to complete his root canal, build up and CAD/CAM crown procedure.

While this procedure typically would take an hour and a half, that day it took a little over two hours, as we prioritize scheduled patients when fitting in same day procedures. But,

Bob walked out of our office a happy man. He didn't have to take more time off of work, reschedule and worry about the procedure for days. He is also extremely grateful to have received his final restoration that same day and left a glowing review for us on Google.

Delivering dentistry the same day it is treatment planned, also known as Same Day Service or SDS, is the most patient-pleasing and profitable way a dental practice can provide treatment.

Before I explain, let me define what Same Day Service means, as it is often confused with Same Day Dentistry. Same Day Dentistry is performing a dental treatment that typically takes multiple visits in one visit. For example, a CAD/CAM crown delivered that day, as opposed to temporizing and seating the crown in a future visit.

Same Day Service, again, is performing a procedure the same day it is diagnosed and treatment planned.

Three reasons why Same Day Services are so important to offer patients include:

1. Drastically reducing patient anxiety
2. Enhancing convenience for patients
3. Significantly increasing your profitability

First, let's look at how Same Day Services address patients' desire for less stressful visits. Anxiety builds over time, so by limiting the time that we have between treatment planning and performing the procedure, Same Day Services can oftentimes make an otherwise stressed patient completely calm during treatment.

Stress tends to act like a locomotive leaving a train station, where it starts slow and then builds into an unstoppable force. So, for almost all anxious patients, by not allowing the stress momentum to ever even start, we can eliminate an enormous amount of anxiety in our offices.

Also, we all have patients that go home and discuss their future care with friends, only to hear their unrelated horror stories. You know these patients who return for care and ask the "I'm not going to have _____ today, am I?" questions, such as "I'm not going to have a root canal after this today, am I?", "I'm not going to owe more than you quoted me today, am I?" and "I'm not going to look like Gary Busey after my veneers today, am I?"

These patients were victims of their friends and family members translating their dental horror stories over to your patient, who likely has a completely different treatment condition. It is best to insulate our patients from this collateral stress whenever possible.

Second, it is blatantly obvious that doing treatment the same day it is diagnosed is more convenient for patients. Usually when talking with doctors about the value of introducing Same Day Services to patients, I get asked, "how do you sell this to patients?"

Selling SDS to patients is easy, as you don't actually sell patients on Same Day Dentistry. SDS sells itself.

All the care team needs to do is offer Same Day Service and people will thank you for it. We are all busy, including patients, so if they can get something done right away, it is best for everyone.

The way my team discusses SDS with patients is simple. Every time we diagnose a procedure that can be done that same day the auxiliary asks, "If Dr. Laskin had time today, would you like to have this done?" If the patient says "yes", then we see if it is feasible to fit into my schedule. If not, we look to see if another dentist has time.

If it seems physically impossible (which is rarely the case), we just apologize and let the patient know we tried to fit them into our schedule today, but we will need to schedule a time later when it is convenient for them.

Just by trying to accommodate Same Day Services in our schedule, we show we care about our patients' time and anxiety, even when we can not perform the dentistry that day.

If we can fit the patient in, we let them know that other patients are already scheduled, so their procedure will likely take longer and they may need to wait for us to get started. I can't think of a time that this was a barrier for a patient to get treatment when their schedule allowed.

Lastly, Same Day Services are incredibly profitable, regardless of the procedures you fit into your day. In fact, they are the most profitable procedures we can perform, as all of our fixed costs are already covered, as well as most of your variable costs. Both your assistant's salary or hourly wage and the rent will be paid whether or not you do that crown today.

So, this revenue comes into your practice with little or no extra expense. That is what makes SDS so profitable.

Also, as stated earlier, anxiety is the primary source of delayed dental treatment. So, offering SDS increases your overall production, as a good portion of the SDS treatment performed would have otherwise been delayed or never completed.

In fact, our research at OperaDDS shows that when an office uses the Chat intra-office communication system to drive Same Day Services, they can get over a whopping 30% increase in production!

The phrase "strike while the iron is hot" is a cliche for the simple reason that it is true. There is never a better time to produce dentistry than the moment a patient says "yes" to treatment. But many dentists worry that this will disrupt *their* schedule and refuse to perform same day treatment, ignoring the damage being done to their patients and their profitability.

I have talked to many, many dentists who at first think they don't have the time in their schedule to fit in patients. I have, however, never talked to a dentist that has actually tried and not found this time.

Believe it or not, there is time to take the case of the crown treatment planned in the hygiene chair and truly "knock it out of the park", combine Same Day Service by doing an immediate CAD/CAM Same Day Dentistry final crown immediately after financial arrangements, all while the patient is relaxing on a virtual beach in Therapeutic Virtual Reality.

12.

The Power of Choice

*"As we look ahead into the next century,
leaders will be those who empower others."*

—Bill Gates

IF MY FAMILY STEPS UP TO THE COUNTER AT THE LOCAL Ben and Jerry's, everyone knows that my daughter, Naiya, will read the menu twelve times, taste six flavors and ask the ice cream scooper his or her opinion before finally narrowing it down to two scoops that don't necessarily go well together.

I will argue, of course, this isn't my wonderful daughter's fault. It is Ben and Jerry's.

The primary reason for Naiya's indecisiveness, I submit, is because ice cream shops give too many options. It has been proven that the more choices we are given, the more complicated making a decision becomes, and the less we like our ultimate choice.

Additionally, too many choices can actually lead to no choice being made at all.[17] So, the unfortunate consequences that result in Ben and Jerry's offering so many choices to their customers include:

1. People have a harder time making a decision
2. Customers end up liking their decision less
3. Many people just don't choose to follow through with a purchase at all

The average dental treatment plan oftentimes looks just like Ben and Jerry's menu.

In addition to having too many options, both "menus" also include terms that you have to burn an ice cream scoop worth of calories to understand what you are even purchasing in the first place.

For example, the average dental patient understands what a "composite resin" is about as much as anyone who doesn't read the description understands the flavors and ingredients in the ice cream "Totally Baked".

Of course we need to give people all their treatment options, as well as the risks and benefits of each option. Luckily, in the vast majority of cases we can achieve this

---

[17] A Tugend, "Too many choices: a problem that can paralyze", Your Money, *New York Times*, 26 February 2010.

fairly easily without overwhelming people, as the number of choices are small compared to the number that would cause choice paralysis.

Research done by Avni M. Shaw and George Wolford showed that given a varied number of roller-ball pens to choose from increased buying behavior until people were given more than 10 options, at which point buying decreased.[18] Since in dentistry we don't have too many cases that have more than ten options, we should certainly be able to give patients options from which they can readily choose.

In cases that have a significant number of treatment options, I would recommend simplifying and clarifying your treatment plans as much as possible. In this way, you can give patients a few good options to choose from before exploring their specific choice in more depth.

Often, I tell patients that they have an extraordinary number of options, but we will go through a process of looking at two or three at a time in order to come up with the option that is best for them. This makes it easy to narrow in on a treatment plan that is right for the patient, but does not overload them to the point of looking through you with a glassy-eyed stare of indecision.

Patients should have more options to tailor their care beyond just treatment plans, however. Whereas treatment

---

[18] AM Shah and G Woolford, "Buying Behaviour as a Function of Parametric Variation of Number of Choices", *Psychol Sci.*, May, 18(5), 369–370 (2007).

plan options are buying decisions, we must also create choices for our patients that address much different needs.

For example, at our office we offer a "comfort menu" that includes comfort items, refreshments and sedation options. This shows people that we care about them as soon as they enter the office.

Being a dental patient puts people in an extremely vulnerable position, which makes many uncomfortable. By giving people choices, you are illustrating that you want the patient to feel empowered. It gives people a sense of control which can put them at ease.

Also, if you are not providing deeper levels of sedation in your office, like IV sedation, I would strongly suggest that you work with someone in your area that does. In my opinion we, collectively, are failing patients today by not offering them enough sedation options. This is another primary reason why people still hate going to the dentist.

Think about it this way; if a patient has a bombed out tooth that I don't feel comfortable treating, I refer that patient to a specialist that can provide the treatment that is needed. But, if a patient is crippled with dental anxiety to the point of making it nearly impossible for the dentist to provide the patient with quality care, and that practice does not provide sedation options, it is viewed as solely the patients' problem.

When we see patients that have more anxiety than we can comfortably treat, I believe it is our moral obligation to either provide patients the deeper sedation options in our office, or refer them to someone who does. This, in my opinion, does not happen enough.

There have been tremendous improvements in the area of dental sedation, and dental anesthesiology is a recognized specialty. It seems to me, however, that fewer dentists are offering sedation options than ever. Many complain about the regulations and hassles involved in offering nitrous oxide or conscious sedation.

While it certainly is not necessary for every office to offer any specific level of sedation, I think that we, as doctors, have a moral obligation to make sure our patients are comfortable enough to receive adequate care.

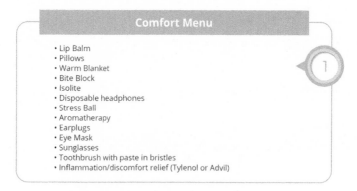

Comfort Menu

- Lip Balm
- Pillows
- Warm Blanket
- Bite Block
- Isolite
- Disposable headphones
- Stress Ball
- Aromatherapy
- Earplugs
- Eye Mask
- Sunglasses
- Toothbrush with paste in bristles
- Inflammation/discomfort relief (Tylenol or Advil)

1

Refreshments

- Water
- Coffee (before or after appointment)
- Tea (before or after appointment)
- Hot Chocolate (before or after appointment)
- Orange Juice (before or after appointment)

2

Sedation Options

- OperaVR Therapeutic Virtual Reality
  - Select OperaVR Adventure to view
    - Adventures: Abstract Chill, Animated Forest, Beach Vacation, Nature Relaxation, World Tour, 360 Experience
- Nitrous Oxide (with or without OperaVR)
  - Requires driver to bring you, stay for procedure and bring you home
  - Requires additional time/cost for procedure
- Oral Sedation
  - Requires driver to bring you, stay for procedure and bring you home
  - Requires additional time/cost for procedure
  - Requires prescription
- IV Sedation
  - Requires driver to bring you, stay for procedure and bring you home
  - Requires additional time/cost for procedure
  - Requires prescription

13.

The 24/7/365 Practice

"Knowledge is a weapon.
I intend to be formidably armed."

—Terry Goodkind

I TRY HARD TO BE A GOOD FATHER, BUT I OFTEN FAIL MY
son, Miles, greatly in one regard; I don't like ball sports.
Consequently, I almost never watch them on TV or pay
attention to how the home teams are doing.

Miles, however, has been obsessed with baseball ever
since I took him to his first game when he was four years
old. During that game, he asked me to break down
every rule and action that happened after every play and
every pitch.

When he played in his first game in little league, he
remained focused, in "ready position", the entire time.

Meanwhile, everyone else on his team was either playing with the grass or picking their nose.

Much to my surprise, not only was Miles focused the entire time during his ballgame, I was too! There is something special about watching your own child play sports, even if you are otherwise not a fan. It is just so much fun to watch your kid and his or her friends out on the field working together as a team.

So, when we got back in the car, I excitedly asked Miles, "Hey, Big Man... what did you think of your first game?".

Miles quietly replied, "Dad, the hardest thing about baseball is my team doesn't know how to play baseball."

I couldn't argue with him.

Fast forward seven years later and Miles was up to bat in the sixth inning of the league finals. The count was two-two when a common, but irritating event happened.

The office emergency phone rang.

My stomach sank as I reached in my pocket and pulled out the phone. The instant I looked at the number, I knew not only exactly who was calling me, but also the conversation I was going to have with the patient on the other end of the line.

Every dentist has "these patients". They seem to have 12 quadrants of MODBL pin retained amalgams that require full coverage restoration, but they choose to do one restoration every six months.

I call these patients the "crown-of-the-month club".

In addition, it seems that every member of the crown of the month club has sensitivity that they complain about every time they come in for a new crown. I don't know if they have overly active nervous systems or just need additional reassurance that everything will be fine, but these patients need a little extra TLC.

Well, this patient was one of the crown-of-the-month club members that would call me the same day she had a crown prepared. Each time she called, I would reassure her that everything would be just fine—and within two days, it was.

But this time the call was right when Miles was up to bat.

I had two options:

1. Pick up the phone and have the conversation that I knew we would have or
2. Send her to voicemail, call her back, likely playing phone tag, while she stresses out, and the obligation to call her back distracts me from my son's performance anyway.

So, I picked up the phone, had the preordained conversation and missed my son's double.

I realized then that our practices are not limited to our physical walls or even bound by office hours. Patients are looking to connect with us everywhere, anytime. This leads to a major problem for our practices.

But, just like in every large problem, therein lies a massive opportunity.

What if you could have an employee that was always available for patients to communicate with your practice 365 days a year, 24 hours a day, that never got sick and cost less than the average front office team member's daily wage? We call that employee the Teledentistry Widget.

The Teledentistry Widget is a feature that gets added to your website and pops up when a patient is viewing your homepage. The widget has a button that asks the simple question, "How can we help you?"

When patients click on the button, they can request to make an appointment, send photos or videos for emergency care or cosmetic consultation, or even have a virtual consultation directly from the website anytime, anywhere on any device.

There is no need for the patient to call and no need to have anyone answer a call from your office.

It is a better way to communicate with patients, both from the perspective of the patient and the care team. All the information the patient puts online is securely stored and automatically put into the patient's chart. It really could not be easier for patients to input the information or for your team to review it.

This isn't some crazy, new technology that may be available "someday". This is available right now and takes less than half an hour to integrate with your existing system.

Taking after hours calls is unnecessary today. You can actually be more accessible to patients, while also being less inconvenienced.

Also, widgets that allow patients to easily connect with your office on your website convert new patients with much higher success than expecting people to contact you by email or phone calls.

Having a feature like the Teledentistry Widget has been reported to increase conversion of new patients approximately 30% more often than if you do not have a similar widget.

Case in point, my patient Joe. Joe hadn't been to the dentist for over 25 years. He needed a full mouth reconstruction. Joe's teeth were so messed up, he didn't need a dentist to tell him he needed help.

Like every patient that hasn't been to the dentist in years, Joe was worried about what it was going to take to fix his mouth. He was also ashamed and thought that he was going to be lectured and berated for his negligence.

Also, like most patients with large dental needs, Joe was ultimately moved to action based on something outside of his mouth. A life event forced him to finally address what he knew he needed to do for quite some time.

Joe's daughter was getting married and he didn't want to be an embarrassment in his daughter's wedding photos. But, he didn't know where to begin to get his teeth fixed and was embarrassed to even ask his friends for a referral.

Joe came to my office for one simple reason: we made it easy for him to send photos from our website to get a quick opinion.

The reason why Joe came to us had absolutely nothing to do with our ability to actually perform the care. It was 100%

the fact that we, after reviewing his photos, communicated quickly to Joe that:

1. We see patients like him all the time (just like any dentist)
2. After he comes to our office and we take a few quick X-rays, we can give him options (just like any dentist)
3. He can choose what, if anything, he would like to do based on his values and financing (just like any dentist) and that
4. There would be no lectures or belittling, only productive conversations (just like any dentist)

You see, we didn't do anything special; we just gave Joe the safe, easy, first step to address his needs.

This led to over $50,000 of dental treatment that took one visit to plan.

In the few appointments that followed, we not only transformed Joe's life and made him proud of his appearance for his daughter's wedding, we also covered over eighty-three years of "wages" for our 24 hours a day, 365 days a year employee, the Teledentistry Widget.

Making it easy for potential new patients to engage with you on your website will increase your new patients and your case acceptance.

For more information about how to engage new patients, and the full list of up to date recommendations on how to generate new patients easily for your practice go to ThePatientFirstManifesto.com/Free

14.

Why Group Practices Are Crushing Small Practices

"Ability is what you're capable of doing.
Motivation determines what you do.
Attitude determines how well you do it."

—Lou Holtz

DURING MY LAST YEAR IN DENTAL SCHOOL, I WORKED as a completely unqualified assistant for Dr. Born. He had seen patients at the office's location for over 50 years and took the practice over from his father, who had been at that same location for over 50 years before him.

There were two operatories in the practice, one lime green and one burnt orange, dating the equipment at over 35 years old. The slow speed handpieces, which were driven by rubber hoses running through pulleys, had been converted from foot pump to electric motor sometime in the 70s.

Therefore, just by looking at the colors of the operatories, you could easily infer that Dr. Born and his father both did not actually look to improve their practice of dentistry for those 100 years. Instead, they were just making the minimal improvements to keep doing dentistry the same way, every day for over a century.

Yes, they each treated patients for five decades a piece; but the practice looked like both Dr. Borns had performed the exact same style of dentistry on all those patients over the course of their careers. In other words, they each had essentially repeated the same year of clinical dentistry fifty times with very little visible improvement.

To truly "practice" dentistry implies looking for continual improvement in your skills and how you provide care. While Dr. Born was a generous, thoughtful caregiver who strived to provide high quality care, his practice had whittled down to very few patients by the time I worked there.

Both of these dentists, father and son, had a love of clinical dentistry and no desire for the business side of care. Even back in the 1990s, this was an extreme detriment to the practice, as the practice was ultimately shut down without any transaction.

Practices like Dr. Born's are closing all the time. Some are purchased and merged into other solo practices. But more and more are either being shut down completely or choosing to partner with corporate dental organizations.

In place of small, one doctor offices, group practices are popping up and absorbing dental practices at an alarming rate. If you ask the average dentist what they think of the largest groups in dentistry, Dental Service Organizations (DSOs), everyone will have an opinion but those opinions will vary greatly. Many will make assumptions that DSOs must deliver lower quality of dental care, while many others will mention how nice it would be to have the operational support, marketing support and group buying discounts.

Contrary to the common belief that all group practices are the same, every DSO is drastically different. Each DSO has its own unique philosophy, different segment of focus, and way that they work with dentists.

But there is a common idea I believe every single DSO knows to be true that the average doctor ignores: there is a tidal wave of consumerism that is overtaking dentistry.

This means that DSOs all believe that the buying decisions that our patients are making outside of dentistry are blending into their dental purchasing decisions more and more every day. And the leaders at DSOs don't just sit in some conference room somewhere theorizing about patients' consumerist behavior; they act on it. This is why many of the leading technologies from teledentistry consultations to AI radiographic diagnoses are being pioneered in the DSO space.

Everyone who works for a group practice knows that a DSOs success directly relies on their ability to deliver high quality dentistry to patients. Just like any other dental practice, if there are unhappy patients, the DSO will fail.

This is not true of our state and national organizations that take hundreds of millions of dollars from dentists, but do not have any direct patient relationship. These aging institutions bill themselves as advocates for our profession, but are really little more than poorly functioning lobbying groups that have deep relationships with the same dental benefit companies that haven't increased reimbursements for patients or practices in over 30 years. Meanwhile, these state and national organizations get massive commissions from their constant marketing efforts, which include trying to sell doctors cars and insurance policies.

In many ways, DSOs are the true organizers of dentistry.

Regardless of what any dentist thinks about the rapid growth of large group practices, DSOs would wither and die if patients don't go to their practices, and they will thrive if patients do.

The same cohort of dentists work within large groups, small groups and single dentist locations. We all get our license from the same overseeing bodies and we all use the same equipment to deliver dentistry.

I think one could argue the quality of care is the same or better in each category. What can not be argued is that the organizational structure of a DSO allows them to focus on the patient perspective more acutely than the average dental practice, who typically does not have the capacity to look at upcoming trends, outside industry knowledge or emerging technologies. Group practices also allow for more convenient patient appointments due to extended and weekend hours, and many times enhanced specialty services housed in the same location as the general practice.

So, what should the average dentist do? I believe that dentists have three options.

First, I think it is absolutely possible for dentists to continue to thrive in a DSO expanding environment. In order to do this, though, they must also act proactively to the trends of rising consumer demand. This involves consistently mapping out a plan where you prioritize how you will improve the patient experience and having consistent implementation protocols.

You can build an office that leverages the advantages of being smaller and having a more nimble, agile business. This is similar to how a local bookstore can certainly compete with Barnes & Noble or Amazon. But, you need to define your practice vision that offers something special, and execute on this vision effectively.

The best option for a small office to differentiate themselves from a large group is to employ technology and services that take longer to deploy and are harder to implement at a larger scale. Ideally, technologies that *patients* notice, like Therapeutic Virtual Reality and CAD/CAM same day restoration (coupled with Same Day Service whenever possible).

Many believe that a key to differentiation for a smaller practice is to be involved locally within your community. I believe that the extra capacity of time and money that DSOs have, however, can actually make them very effective at this too.

So, I recommend that any solo practitioner looking to maintain their autonomy in today's consumeristic dental marketplace focus primarily on implementing technology that is harder to roll out at scale or requires more team training to adopt effectively.

Second, dentists can either start or join a group practice. Remember, there are no two DSOs that are alike, so interview many and see if there is a good fit for you.

Check out organizations like the Association of Dental Support Organizations and the Dentist Entrepreneur Organization to find groups and see if there is a good fit for you.

If you don't find the right fit and you are particularly entrepreneurial, you can look to start your own group. Small and mid-sized dental groups are the fastest growing segment of our industry today and there is a lot of room for future growth in this segment.

In my experience, I had interviewed several DSOs and did not find the right fit, so I started my own DSO with the idea that it would grow to 5-10 practices before looking for a transition. It was only two months into my buying the second location under the umbrella of my new group when I met the leadership team at Dental Care Alliance.

I realized quickly that I had found the right fit for me. After a few months of discussion, my practices were merged with DCA, where I am happy to continue working today. Affiliating with DCA has allowed me to focus on just the aspects of dentistry that I want to, as well as open up my capacity to explore new opportunities.

For me, the leadership of the organization I would join was crucially important to my decision and DCA has the best leadership I have found in a dental group.

Finally, you can bury your head in the sand, ignore the obvious trend that our patients are becoming more savvy shoppers for their care and act like that there is no need to "adjust the sails" of your practice to the winds of change.

Given that this lack of action has historically been the choice of the overwhelming majority of dentists and it has worked out OK for them thus far, I believe that most will follow this path.

However, I also believe that these dentists will deeply regret their choice or, more accurately, lack of decision.

There are many trends that we have explored in this book that foreshadow the average dentist's regret about not adapting to the reality of new patient expectations. From demanding more convenient hours, not tolerating painful procedures, wanting more options in their care, and the overarching idea that people today are judging their experience in our offices to every other consumer experience they have, we can assume that patients will be seeking out better dental experiences at an accelerating rate.

In fact, the number of patients that changed doctors because of a poor dental experience has increased 40% in 2020 alone.[19]

---

[19] "2020 Healthcare Consumer Experience Study", Cedar, 2020.

Steve Jobs once asked, "If today were the last day of your life, would you want to do what you are about to do today?"

I would ask you to look closely at your practice and ask yourself the question, "What have I done today that will allow me to do what I want for the rest of my life?"

The choice is yours: will you put your patients first and act to implement the easy solutions that allow your practice to thrive or go to work tomorrow, do nothing and hope that nobody notices.

To get started implementing technology and procedures that patients expect today, go to ThePatientFirstManifesto.com/Free

15.

How to Successfully Implement New Initiatives

As the great cartoon philosopher G.I. Joe said, "knowing is half the battle".

In other words, understanding any opportunity or need in your practice is only a fraction of what is necessary to achieve success. The other, and frankly much more challenging, part of addressing any required change lies in successfully implementing that new technology, process or procedure.

Every practice has that piece of technology that was purchased to address some need, but it sits in a closet unused. But that same technology is being used every day successfully in other practices and the doctors that use it claim it transformed their practice. Why does this happen?

A common response tends to vilify the salespeople that convince doctors to incorporate these procedures in the first place. I think selling transformative technology to dentists, but not being an experienced dentist yourself, is an incredibly difficult position to be in. Most doctors are perfectionists by nature, which makes convincing them to change a very difficult proposition.

Yet, some offices incorporate all emerging technology and procedures seemingly effortlessly. Do these offices know something that the other practices don't? The answer is yes, they do.

They understand that there are simple steps that must be followed in order to incorporate change into their practice. Steps that, if ignored, will cause any new improvement in your practice to fail.

Learning to effectively alter anything in your practice first requires acknowledging that any change will have some pain associated with it; no matter how small the change is. In change theory, this pain is called the "Valley of Despair".

The Valley of Despair defines the fact that every time you incorporate change, you will be slowed down and experience the discomfort of doing something different. Even if the change is better in every way possible, the mere process of doing something new requires us to stop and think.

Humans have evolved over millions of years to hate slowing down and thinking; this is why change is so hard for all of us. All change hurts.

Understanding what the specific downsides are to any new process you bring into your practice is vitally important to your ultimate success in implementing that procedure.

For example, if you are going to ask your receptionist to answer the phone tomorrow in the exact same way as

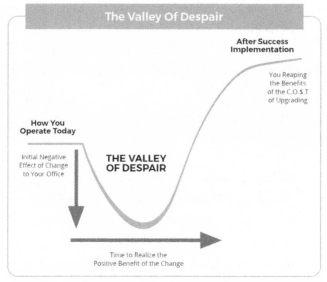

to find out more about incorporating change and the C.O.$.T. benefits of upgrading your practice go to ThePatientFirstManifesto.com/Free

yesterday, using the same script, except add either "good morning" or "good afternoon" how would you go about implementing it?

Just asking your receptionists to do this once will likely fail. Sure, it may work for a week or two, but then everyone tends to slide back to where they were once comfortable before the change; especially when the next change is brought forth.

The Valley of Despair will take over, shoving your front desk team back to their comfort zone of ease and less work by not acknowledging the time of day when greeting patients on the phone.

The way to successfully implement change in your office and overcome the Valley of Despair is to have a plan of action that works for every new technology and procedure.

Here is my ten step plan that I have found works for just about every practice:

1. **Define success -** You must understand clearly why you are going through the pain of doing something new, so that it will be easier to navigate the Valley of Despair and come out on the other side successfully. If you do not know the size of the prize on the other side of this discomfort, you and your team will likely lose motivation once you hit the depths of the Valley.

2. **"Presell" the change to your team -** Everybody affected by the new technology or procedure is about to experience the discomfort of change, so selling them on the new technology or procedure will allow them to rally around the cause. The idea of something new can be a powerful motivation for the best care team members, so make sure to get your key people excited about what you are implementing as soon as possible.

3. **Communicate to the entire team -** Cascading what success looks like and what is in it for your entire team is vital to getting them onboard to implement change in order to reap the benefits of any new technology or procedure. We must travel through the

Valley of Despair together, or whatever you are looking to incorporate in your practice is probably not
going to work. Nobody should be left out; even if it is
a clinical change, make sure to let the business team
members know the benefits and vice versa.

4. **Determine how you will communicate the benefit to your patients** - Often, this step is overlooked,
as the benefits to patients can be completely different
than they are for doctors or team members. For example, our CBCT X-ray system allows for exquisitely
accurate implant treatment planning, but most patients
in our office don't really understand this or even need
an implant. The most useless view of the cone beam
imaging system for me, the three dimensional view of
the skull, just looks plain cool to patients, who "ooh"
and "aah" everytime they see it for the first time. Just
showing every new patient their own jaw in 3D let's
them know we leverage technology in our practice—
especially the part of the software that I never use.

5. **Commit** - Definitely utilize short, easily reversible
trials whenever possible when evaluating technology
prior to committing to full implementation. Once the
decision is made, it will require dedication by you and
your team to see the change through. Never just "try
something out", unless you are in a trial period and still
evaluating if you are even going to try and implement
the change. It should be communicated to your team
that you aren't just testing the change, it's happening

whether they like it or not. Too many great technologies and procedures are not implemented because of team members who lacked the vision to see past the Valley of Despair.

6. **Identify and lift any barriers** - Prior to implementing the technology, obtain a list of any bottlenecks or barriers that can be lifted for a successful launch. This includes software/hardware requirements, updating systems, firewall restrictions, new required training, armamentarium, etc. Remove all barriers prior to implementing the change, or the likelihood of failure goes up exponentially.

7. **Assign a champion** - A single person must be accountable for a successful integration of the change. It is important that only one person is accountable, as it is too easy for people to collectively accept failure. If one person stands up and claims to be the champion, they take ownership of the new initiative. The champion often needs to ask for assistance from others, but everyone should know who is in charge of the successful implementation. On the other side of the Valley of Despair, when you have hit the success you defined in Step 1 above, the champion should be celebrated in front of the whole team for their leadership.

8. **Make space in your schedule -** You will need to slow down, in order to speed up. Make sure you devote 100% of your and your team's attention to successful implementation, as change does not happen without

accounting for the time required to process and incorporate it.

9. **Get enough -** Some technologies require multiple units to successfully implement. If you have ten hygienists and only one digital X-ray sensor, everyone will just keep using film. Scarcity in a new technology leads to team members assuming it is not available, so it will go unused.

10. **Do research prior to implementation -** Learning whatever you can before you start the implementation process will allow for a deeper level of conversation and knowledge in the time spent during implementation. If you are incorporating a new CAD/CAM system, for example, go online and watch videos or talk with users of the system before you take delivery of your new "toy".

to learn more about how to successfully implement anything new in your practice and get your Upgrade Implementation Checklist go to ThePatientFirstManifesto.com/Free

The Upgrade Growth Roadmap

THERE ARE SOME TECHNOLOGIES THAT ARE NECESSARY today if you want to be considered a modern dental practice in the eyes of your patients. Luckily these are almost all low-cost (or free) and easy-to-implement technologies that will grow your practice.

Many dentists wonder where to start and what next steps are necessary to take action and address dental patients' desires. Now that you more completely understand the power of leveraging simple, but crucial aspects of patient care that lie outside of solely clinical quality, I would like to help get you started.

I've put together the Upgrade Dental Growth Roadmap that maps out every technology available in dentistry, in the order that I believe it should be implemented, along with implementation tips for each technology on the Roadmap.

The Upgrade Dental Growth Roadmap is divided into three distinct levels:

Level 1 Includes low cost and easy-to-implement technologies that provide "no-brainer" wins that directly grow your bottom line. Level 1 technologies are what I believe every practice should minimally have available for patients. In other words, if you do not have all these technologies, you are in danger of being outdated and losing patients.

Level 2 Includes moderately expensive or somewhat difficult-to-implement upgrades for your practice. Level 2 upgrades should be considered once you have covered all the aspects in Level 1. If you consider your practice to be forward thinking at all, or you plan to market your practice as "high-tech", I believe that implementing all of the Level 2 items is essential.

Level 3 Upgrades include technologies that put you ahead of the curve and unlock the full potential of your practice. Level 3 upgrades typically are more rare for offices to implement, but they can provide incredible benefits and profits if you and your team are willing to go the extra mile for your patients.

Given that you are one of the few, exceptional doctors, team members or patients that made it this far, I want to make sure that you get the most up to date information available.

To that end, to get the Upgrade Dental Growth Roadmap, as well as details on all of the crucial-to-implement Level 1 technologies on the Roadmap, be sure to go to *ThePatientFirstManifesto.com/Free.*

The pace of change in dental technology has been accelerating exponentially, and I do not believe it is going to slow down anytime soon. So, a key component to both putting patients first and to growing your practice is to continually keep track of new emerging technologies, both within dentistry and in other industries. In that way, you can decide what is right for your practice and your patients.

Failing to keep track of new technologies and techniques in dentistry will lead to you falling behind.

To get the most current Upgrade Dental Growth Roadmap and for more information about any of these technologies, including short video trainings on each one that includes recommendations for technology choice and implementation, go to ThePatientFirstManifesto.com/Free

Afterward

UNFORTUNATELY, BEING A CARING, SKILLED CLINICIAN is not enough to have a successful practice today. Sadly, many gifted dentists have withering practices and are left not knowing why they are having financial difficulties or why their teams are frustrated and stressed out.

My hope is that The Patient First Manifesto helps doctors and care team members who provide high quality care in their practices to understand more deeply the shifting consumer mindset of our patients.

My goal in releasing this book is to help grow those practices that are devoted to excellence in their clinical care. If we expand the practices that are focused on quality care, we can increase their impact and help more patients receive better dental care.

My ultimate goal is to bury the common notion that dentistry is painful and that going to the dentist needs to be a negative experience. The tremendous advancements in dental care delivery seem to have made little impact in the patients' perspective of what it means to go to the dentist. This is unacceptable and problematic for doctors, care team members and patients.

Being a dental professional is hard work that requires being proficient in many different skill sets. Performing microsurgies in the mouths of people who are filled with anxiety, in a reclined, vulnerable position while your face is less than a foot away from theirs is stressful, at best. Layer on top of that our time and financial challenges and the fact we lead an entire team working under these conditions, and it is obvious why many practices have difficulty incorporating new technology and procedures.

I know how it feels to lose sleep over a complicated case or whether you will be able to pay your bills at the office. The Patient First Manifesto seeks to aid good practices from being victims of a rapidly changing marketplace, and to instead arm doctors and teams with the information needed to thrive in this environment. If these practices grow, they will in turn positively transform more patients' and team members' lives.

Thank you for being an engaged member of the caregiving team. It is only through the difficult work of adaptation and innovation that we, collectively, can stop patients from ever uttering the phrase "I hate the dentist".

I'm grateful for all the amazing doctors, clinical team members, business team members, consultants, vendors, educators and partners that understand that if we put patients first, we all thrive together.

When patients win, we all win.

Additional Resources

The 5 Minute Practice Makeover

In this video course of five videos under ten minutes each, you will find out why most dentists don't hit their goals and what to do about it. This training includes tips and tricks on how to skyrocket case acceptance rates and increase productivity in your dental practice.

The Upgrade Dental Growth Roadmap

This course includes 23 separate videos, one for each upgrade category for dentistry, divided into three levels. Level 1 includes low cost and easy-to-implement upgrades that every office should have in their practice. Level 2 showcases moderately expensive or challenging-to-implement upgrades that should come after Level 1 is complete. Level 3 includes key technologies to unlock the full potential of your practice and truly place you ahead of the curve. Each video includes how to evaluate if the technology is right for you, as well as gives a specific recommendation for adoption. Partner companies whose products are recommended within this series often provide the best offer they have available within this training.

How To Give Painless Injections

This course addresses the number one reason why people hate going to the dentist: the needle. In order to have a thriving practice today, you are required to effectively manage your patients' discomfort. In this video series, Dr. Laskin explains the art of the painless injection, including several new technologies that make painless dentistry finally a reality. Nothing promotes word of mouth referrals better than transforming people's expectations about what it means to be a dental patient, and mastering local anesthetic is the easiest way to improve people's experiences in your office.

Simplifying Composites Training

Quadrants of composites can be frustrating and not seem profitable. In this course you will learn the keys to simplifying any composite appointment, making composites more predictable and more profitable. Recent developments in composite technology are highlighted, showcasing ways to minimize inventory in your office and difficulty in placement of resin restorations. Additionally, new developments in composite composition are covered, which make shade matching during esthetic procedures drastically easier.

Paperless Processes for Team Members

Getting the team on board with any new process is imperative, or you will likely fail to implement the change. This course, led by Abby Frey, CRDA, speaks directly to the care team and describes the importance of a paperless office. The benefits for team members and patients are highlighted, so that everyone in your office will all agree that it is time to ditch the clipboard and offer a better experience for your patients.

Controlling Anxiety Without Drugs

It has been reported that over 60% of Americans have anxiety about going to the dentist and nothing has fundamentally been done about this for about a century. We, in dentistry, have relied on drugs or patients' grit to address this disastrous reality for too long. In this course you will learn the keys to melting patients' anxiety so that you can produce higher quality care more efficiently on patients that are much more comfortable. Not only will your patients be less stressed out; you will be healthier and your team will be more relaxed to work with too.

The Talentship Live Workshop

If you want to maximize your team's efficacy, while being surrounded by interesting peers that understand the inherent power in leadership, this six-hour live-person course is for you. You will learn how to quantify skills and map out your team's capabilities, so that you can identify and address any bottlenecks. You will gain the ability to empower each individual member of your practice to showcase their unique skill sets and how they fit into your care team. You will finally gain clarity in what people do and how proficient they are at their job. Never again will you need to give out raises just because the Earth has made another orbit around the Sun.

Become a Certified Talentship Guide

If you are a consultant that either has a focus on leadership and skills development, or you would like to be one, apply to become a Certified Talentship Leadership Guide. Talentship Leadership Guides are granted access to training materials after being interviewed and then listed in our website for offices to contact you. Offices and companies looking to certify members of their team may also apply.

Find out more at ThePatientFirstManifesto.com/Free